THE STORY OF EARLY MAN

H. E. L. MELLERSH

———

The Story of
EARLY MAN

*Human Evolution to the End
of the Stone Age*

———

ILLUSTRATIONS BY SALLY MELLERSH

NEW YORK : THE VIKING PRESS : 1960

Published in 1960 by The Viking Press, Inc.
625 Madison Avenue, New York 22, N.Y.

Published in England under the title *The Story of Man*

Library of Congress catalog card number: 60-5837

Printed in the U.S.A. by The Murray Printing Company

Contents

Note on Illustrations

The locations of drawings, diagrams, and maps are indicated in the index by asterisks.

The endpaper design is based on figures from Spanish rock paintings.

THE STORY OF EARLY MAN

Ye shall be as gods, knowing good and evil.

Genesis, iii. 5

Introduction

Man as part of life: we do not in truth often think in those terms; rather we think of life revolving about man.

Up to a point we are right in so doing. Biologists and evolutionists and lesser breeds with longer names are fond of telling us that man is a usurper, a parvenu, that if all Earth's time were a day then man arrived in the last second or so. That is indeed significant. But it is not overwhelmingly significant, for no human being can really visualize or understand a span of a million years, let alone a few thousand millions. Time in fact is not everything. The moment when Christ was born, the hour when Shakespeare wrote a sonnet, the day when Churchill's *few* saved civilization, all those are of vastly greater importance than a million years without a name in which brontosaurus mindlessly browsed and tyrannosaurus as mindlessly savaged and killed.

It is not time that is paramount but events, and human events at that. At least so we must believe, or else sacrifice all self-respect in living. And since we are ourselves, to whit the only creatures who can read and write and talk and reasonably think, then there is no more to be said: what we say about ourselves *goes*—and if by chance every syllable of it is balderdash we shall never know, nor for that matter will the bigger and better saurians that may have come back should we be so foolish as to destroy ourselves.

That, I respectfully suggest, is the double-sided attitude to foster by those who read this book: man is indeed the 'only creature who can read and write and talk and reasonably think', a creature in fact different from all the rest; but man is also part of the animal kingdom, as surely and unalterably as are ape and ass, beetle and batrachian and bird. Let this be set out clearly, as in a textbook, as a 'visual aid'—as a caption, if you will, that appears, wobbling ever so slightly, on your television screen:

13

Man is an animal
BUT
Man is an animal *plus*

And the answer to the question, 'plus what?' is: plus, essentially, a bigger brain. This is, of course, not the only excellent thing added to man's birthright: he has a supple and well co-ordinated body, an expressive countenance, most beautiful skill of hand and eye. Nor is 'bigger' brain an adequate epithet. His is a different brain, admittedly superior in no more than degree, yet in so great a degree as to constitute something virtually new in the world. That idea is one that this book will have to elaborate with care.

It will do so, though, with no anguished and breast-beating cries of apology. Many who noticed the previous book, *The Story of Life*, to which this is in the way of a sequel, described it as tracing the course of Evolution up to its culmination in Man and then added some such phrase as 'if indeed that can be called a culmination'. It is becoming a fashion to apologize for ourselves, so great is our fear, so great is our sense of guilt. It is not for this book to philosophize on current world events, nor is it perhaps much more than irresponsibility to suggest that if we do indeed blow ourselves up it will be at any rate an almighty bang that will shake God in his seat. But we have not done it yet and we may never do it; the chances are, I believe, that we shall never do it. And for the rest: we are, really, genuinely, clever—and potentially wise. Do not let us in our fear and uncertainty forget that; for if we do then we present to ourselves an untrue picture. Man, for good or ill, is doing something that no other form of life has done except in the most modest and elementary way, he is controlling his environment.

If man controls his environment then his evolutionary story is an entirely different evolutionary story from any enacted before. That is undoubtedly another idea for the reader to be reminded of before he starts this book. All who recount the story of life's unfolding on this planet, having made great play with the Primate line, and the hominids, and *Parapithecus* and *Sinanthropus* and the rest, end up triumphantly but abruptly with *Homo sapiens*. The natural question is: 'And does Evolution stop there?' The answer is that of course it does not. But the answer is too that the questioner must now expect a very different story. There is a new slant, a great shift. The gates,

14

in terms of the old myth, have clanged to. The slow, unreflective, natural life of the Garden of Eden is over; the new creation, 'knowing good and evil', faces his environment, and is aware of it.

He is aware of it with a new instrument, his brain. Once more, because it is so important: man had inherited a *new thing*, conscious, reflective, imagining mind. And note that it is indeed inherited, it is evolved: new, but growing out of the old. Dogs surely dream, apes weep, the seal loves music, the horse trembles with excitement,

> he saith among the trumpets, Ha, ha;
> and he smelleth the battle afar off.

But man is blessed and cursed with an instrument that is as a grand piano to a one-stringed lute, as an electronic computor to an abacus, cinemascope to a magic lantern, or an eagle's wing to the clumsy stretched leather of a not very cleverly vol-planing pterodactyl: in two words a marvellous instrument.

Indeed almost at times an overwhelming instrument. In trying to trace man's early struggles to control his environment and to be a man, one gets I think the inescapable impression that man's mind troubled him, was sometimes almost too much for him, as an imaginative and temperamental youngster can be too much for his parents. He did some queer things and must have thought some queer thoughts. At times he seems to have delighted in making life difficult for himself, even to torture himself.

Yet he succeeded. He came into the world unarmed, with but one talent which all too truly was death to hide, lodged, but fortunately not useless, in the little bulging box of his cranium; and he succeeded. To make out of the brittle and resistant flint a fletcher's and a hunter's kit, later a carpenter's, was to succeed. To refine copper, to make an alloy with tin, to cast and forge bronze, was to succeed. So too was it to paint the cave walls of Lascaux and Altamira, to fashion the 'Venus of Willendorf', to raise Stonehenge and the megalithic tombs of the Atlantic coast—artistic and architectural successes. But what men did with these their creations, and why they created them, is, so far as we can see, often strange and sometimes misguided.

Perhaps we are wrong in so thinking; though we must surely

try to understand. The trouble is that we do not always know what were the actions and intentions of prehistoric man; indeed in detail and with exactitude we can never know.

But then we do not know in detail or with exactitude the thoughts and actions of Napoleon at Waterloo: between history and pre-history the difference is only one of degree, though admittedly a large degree. There is, too, the help that can be given to us by the still-living or recently living peoples whose way of life is or was the way of

The Venus of Willendorf—comfort-able, unforgettable, not entirely un-contemporary

the paleolithic hunter or the neolithic herdsman. The anthropologist can help when the archaeologist becomes silent.

That is indeed what this book will try to do, combine anthro-pology and archaeology so to present a picture of the emergence of man and of his mind and of his spirit. I am aware that it is a danger-ous path to tread, that indeed many experts would say that this is a wrong thing to do since our knowledge is not yet great enough. But they will probably always go on saying that; and the layman has a right to be served. Even if the picture is only 80 per cent right when he gets it and 60 per cent in ten years' time, that is better than a complete blank—or, not to be rude to the layman, better than a few hard points of detail connected by no more than a shifting, whirling and confusing mist. We shall have to tread delicately at times—and with hope of a better fate than Agag's.

The book will begin by tracing man's inheritance, of body, of brain and sensitivity, of environment. It will end when neither man nor his mind seem any longer properly describable as primitive or prehistoric, when the Stone Ages are past and at least the scent of civilization is in the air.

1

Evidence for Ancestry

I s it really true that we, the species *Homo sapiens*, are not a separate creation but have arrived by a series of what Charles Darwin called modifications?

Do not be impatient at this apparently naive question. For to be scientific as it were at second-hand—a lilo scientist let alone an armchair one, drowsily wolfing great gobbets of scientific facts without savouring them—is certainly not a good thing. And in particular how dull it is to accept lethargically the extraordinary idea that we are descended from the animals.

For it is an extraordinary idea; one that remained incredible to nearly all men until a hundred years ago and to a good number of them after that. Man has a soul, he is made in the image of God, he is not as the beasts that perish: *that* is the whole tenor of the Christian, Western tradition to which we are heir. The new beliefs, based on new knowledge, do not necessarily seek to destroy that tradition; but if they are to act as a leaven to it and not as a poison they surely need some pretty careful scrutiny.

Let us therefore cultivate and encourage some initial critical disbelief; and then let us seek to destroy our disbelief by sound proof, so that we may realize all the better the strangeness and novelty of the conception that we are surveying: man as a part of the animal world, evolved and evolving. What is the evidence?

The best and most striking evidence will come from the Earth, into which all life sinks back to decay and to start the cycle all over again. Or rather the Earth will furnish evidence when by a combination of chances life fails to decay and so becomes the incontrovertible evidence of a fossil—something which says, *this has lived*.

But there is also the physiological and anatomical evidence, the

19

evidence of likeness of bodily form. That is familiar stuff: let us deal with it first, and shortly.

The great thing is to think in terms of *pattern*. Life, once it had got going from small beginnings, invented various bodily patterns with which to take advantage the more efficiently of its environment. Whatever is the purposive force or lack of purposive force behind organic evolution, it is I think legitimate in this sort of generalized surveying to personify life. There is no sinister motive; I am not trying to inculcate 'Neo-Lamarckism'. The starfish is, for example, a form strikingly different from our own; one could call it the spoked

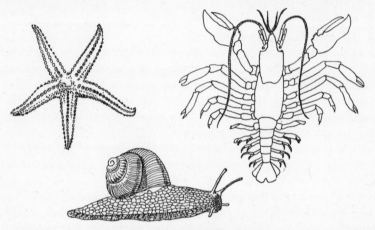

Animal patterns, other than our own

or circular pattern, with radiating limbs and the seats of sensitivity and ingestion—head and body—in the middle. The mollusc is a sort of patternless pattern, amorphous soft body or lump of muscle protected by shell. Then one of the most successful patterns, in point of variety and ubiquity *the* most successful pattern, is the arthropod, the jointed-limbed. These insects and arachnids and crustaceans give themselves an outside protective skeleton and achieve skill and mobility by a battery, a multiplicity, of jointed appendages. Finally —for this is enough for our survey—there comes the vertebrate, who put his skeleton and his joints inside his body, gave himself not only a head for his sensitivities but a box, the brain-case, to put them in, and developed the symmetrical pattern of paired limbs about the central flexible line and fulcrum of a backbone.

That is of course where we come into the picture. We share this ground plan with fish, amphibian, reptile, mammal; indeed we keep the pattern beautifully unimpaired: how like we are for instance to the lowly frog, except that he chooses to fringe his limbs not with five useful appendages, digits, but with four.

Nor of course is bodily ground plan the only criterion of likeness. We are mammals: we too have red blood, have warm blood—of an even temperature so long as we are alive and well—we too develop our young babes within the female womb and when they come to

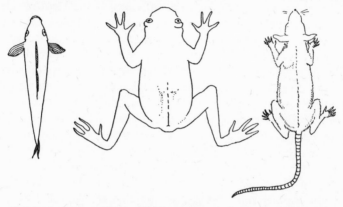

The successful vertebrate pattern: head and backbone, with limbs (or fins) attached

face the outside world suckle and protect them. To shift the point that Shylock made, we are indeed

'fed with the same food, hurt with the same weapons, subject to the same diseases, healed by the same means, warmed and cooled and by the same winter and summer.'

Yes, and very much blessed or cursed with the same 'organs, dimensions, senses, affections, passions', to which fact any discerning keeper of pets will be only too anxious to testify.

The point does not need to be laboured. In their pattern and function all vertebrates and in particular all mammalian forms of life connect; and men are most certainly vertebrate and mammalian. In two ways—in composition of the blood, and in detail of skeleton, almost bone for bone—do men and the rest of the family of Primates particularly connect.

21

And let common sense reinforce the scientific evidence. After all, much of the latter is relatively modern, and the fact that wise and knowledgeable men have throughout most of history held an opposite view is not in the least an argument in favour of its truth. Up to a couple of centuries ago, who for that matter had seen a Primate, tree shrew, lemur, tarsier, monkey, anthropoid ape, let alone dissected one? Then, too, most of the rest of the mammals have so gone in for specialization—disguised their digitated limbs as hooves, stumps, flippers, wings, changed their teeth and jaws, grown their neck as the giraffe or their proboscis as the elephant—that their initial ground-plan is hardly recognizable and their cousinship to ourselves not easily apparent. Nowadays however, with our immensely increased modern knowledge, we are simply forced to ask ourselves: how else in all reasonableness could man have come into existence other than by a slow modification of earlier forms of life? Completely new forms of life do not suddenly appear upon the Earth: creation just does not work that way, and we of this generation inescapably know it. Georges Cuvier, one of the last of the great naturalists to insist stubbornly, in the face of fossil evidence, in the immutability of species, had to invent, in order to justify his beliefs, a series of revolutions or catastrophes that wiped the slate of life clean for another start. We realize now that though there were indeed such revolutions in the Earth's climate they did not spell death to all existing life but rather only to the unadaptable and over-specialized, affording on the contrary great opportunity to the evolutionary urge to set out on fresh courses: 'creation' indeed, but building on the old and not impossibly *de novo*. In such a way indeed must the small insignificant proto-mammal have taken its opportunity when, nearly a hundred million years ago, the long Paleozoic Era began to break up and the dragons, the brainless and fantastic saurians, began to die. Then with the mammals came the ascendency of mother-love, and education of the young, and brain. At that time, surely, though he may have had to wait a long while to come upon the scene, was man created in the womb of time. As the late Professor Joad might well have said, it all depends upon what you mean by 'created'.

Very well then. Man must have been created by evolution from other and earlier forms of mammalian life: a strange and not easily digested truth, though there it is. What we want to know is, *how* did it happen? We come to the fossil, the down-to-earth evidence. In plain fact the evidence is sparse, with many gaps. Of course from the old-fashioned, 'where is the missing link?' point of view the evidence is the reverse of sparse; there is a surfeit of links, perhaps a better simile would be to say a tangle of links. But when we wish to trace in detail the steps between ourselves and that assumed ancestor of ours which Darwin cautiously described as 'a hairy, tailed quadruped, probably arboreal in habits', then the evidence is still inadequate. It is so for two very good reasons: many of the likely places on the Earth's surface in which to find the evidence have not yet been searched; and skeletons fossilize only in the very particular sort of circumstance—the slow covering by mud or silt for instance —into which the intelligent and lively higher Primate is not likely to allow his body to fall.

Now how far back do we go, and what exactly are we looking for? There is a danger here, a gaping and bristling trap into which many have fallen, the trap of looking for what one wants to find. It is natural that there should have been this trouble for we not only are uncertain as to what we are looking for but also have a personal and passionate interest in the result. The annals of physical anthropology are strewn with stories of wishful thinkings, presumptuous claims, quarrels, sulks, hoaxes. That they are also strewn with stories of the most patient, disciplined and dedicated work goes without saying for anyone who while realizing that scientists are human knows something of their tradition and method of work.

The guiding principle for those who are searching for their ancestors is that Evolution does not work backwards: it does not ever seem to work from more specialization to less. However the elephant got his trunk, it is supremely unlikely that the organ will ever during the generations shrink again; no descendant of the horse is going to regrow its five toes. If, then, in casting around for something to work upon, we compare ourselves to the other existing Primates, we must constantly bear in mind that we are comparing end products with end products and that if, to take simple examples, a fossil skeleton were found with very long arms and a shrunken thumb or enormous ridges down the sides of its cranium it would much more probably be a progenitor of that arboreal expert the gibbon or that heavy-jawed monster the gorilla than of man.

Indeed probably the most healthy initial exercise for the would-be physical anthropologist is to visit a museum and to study the skeletons of man and of modern anthropoid ape. True there is similarity bone for bone; that point it is right to stress. But for the rest the significant fact is not likeness but contrast. In the words of Sir Wilfred Le Gros Clark, whose wise guidance in these matters we are shortly to be following, there are two kinds of characteristics, those of 'common inheritance' and those of 'independent acquisition', and it is supremely important in this business of studying and comparing anatomies in the search for our ancestors that we try to distinguish the one from the other.

Gibbon and gorilla: ape's *difference from* man

As for how far back we should go, the answer is, I think: for our purpose, for the purpose of understanding human history, not very far. That we belong to the Family of Primates as well as to the Order of Mammals is of considerable importance and we shall return to the fact when we consider the growth of senses and sensitivities; but as to whether we stem more directly from this or that mammal of fifty to a hundred million years ago is a question which need not concern us very much—and is probably insoluble anyway. What does concern us is to cast out for good that hard-dying misconception that our ancestor was an anthropoid ape, some grotesque mixture, one imagines, of chimpanzee, gorilla and orang-utan. As well expect an early Rolls-Royce to be a cut between a Jaguar, a Fordson and a Mo-ped. We must progress even further and cease

SOME EVIDENCE OF OUR ANCESTRY

Name	Where found	When found	What found	Believed number of years old	Names of discoverers most closely connected	Remarks
Parapithecus	Egypt	1910	A lower jaw	? 40 million	Schlosser	Monkey-sized; teeth not like modern apes
Proconsul	Egypt	1931–48	Almost complete skull	? 20 million	Leakey	Size of small chimpanzee. Perhaps a runner rather than a tree-liver
Dryopithecus	Europe and India	1850 onwards	Skulls and a few limb bones	? 10 million	Lartet	An anthropoid ape of a generalized form
Australopithecus	Bechuanaland and Transvaal	1925 onwards	Many skulls; hip and other bones. Also baboon skulls, but no flint tools	½ million or more	Dart and Broom	More human skull and near-upright stance. Age hard to estimate
Pithecanthropus	Java and China	1899 and 1931 onwards	Ultimately, almost complete skulls; hip and other bones. Also bones of deer, and primitive quartz tools	½ million or less	Dubois; Black; Wiedenreich; Koenigswald	Rather more humanly shaped skull; walked erect. Evidence of use of fire. Includes Sinanthropus
Heidelberg Man	Germany	1907	Lower jaw. Also horse and rhino bones	? 400,000	Schötensack	Massive jaw; near-human teeth
Atlanthropus	Algiers	1954	Two lower jaws with many teeth missing. Also animal bones and early type of 'hand-axe'	? 200,000	Arambourg	Shape of jaw is human. First bones to be found with the standard 'hand-axe'
Steinheim Man	Germany	1933	Most of a skull	? 50,000	Berckhemers	Seems to be an anatomical link between Pithecanthropus and Homo sapiens
Neanderthal Man	Europe, Africa, Asia	1848 onwards	Ultimately, complete skeletons. Also mammoth and bison bones and Mousterian flints	? 150,000 to 20,000	Boule	In the 'extreme' type certainly not our ancestor
Aurignacian Man (Homo sapiens)	France, etc.	1850 onwards	Complete skeletons. Also bones of reindeer, etc., and many flint tools	? 20,000	Lartet Boucher de Perthes	The first of the paleolithic cave painters

to expect what the earlier evolutionists expected, interpreting Darwin too simply and with the horrible hoax of the Piltdown Man to bedevil them, that as we trace backwards we shall find our ancestors consistently and steadily more 'ape-like' in all respects. Why should we?

Here, since in this matter we are being as plain and factual as possible, we will put down the finds in the form of a table. It is not by any manner of means comprehensive; and it will be obvious from what has just been said that it is not, in fact it cannot be, authoritarian. I have given among other information the dates of discovery and the names of the anthropologists most intimately concerned; these may help the reader to tie up with other descriptions that he may have come across in books or newspapers and magazines.

There are a few preliminary things to say about this table. The first is that our possible ancestors are included as well as our probable. Secondly, there is a big gap of something like ten million years between Dryopithicus, a fossil ape of way back in the Tertiary Era,* and Australopithecus who as we shall see has good claim to be considered at least half-man.

The third point to remember is that *what* is found—anything from a single tooth to a whole skeleton—is obviously a considerable guide to the importance of the discovery and the degree of certainty with which theories can be based upon it. For instance the Heidelberg find is a lower jaw only, not a great deal on which to base theories though perhaps more than the uninitiated would imagine. Jaws and teeth are the most frequent finds, and those fortunately are

---

* The four main Eras of geological time as recognized by scientists are: Primary or *Paleozoic* ('Ancient Life', ending about 200 million years ago); Secondary or *Mesozoic* ('Middle Life', ending about 70 million years ago, sometimes called the era of the giant reptiles); Tertiary or *Cenozoic* ('New' or 'Recent Life', i.e. the era of the mammals), [ending about one million years ago; and Quaternary, the era of the entrance of man. Tertiary and Quaternary are divided into Periods as follows:

Era	Period	Approx. date of beginning in millions of years ago	Meaning
Cenozoic or Tertiary	Eocene ..	70	Dawn of recent (life)
	Oligocene ..	50	A few of recent
	Miocene ..	35	Less of recent
	Pliocene ..	15	More of recent
Quaternary	Pleistocene ..	1	Most of recent
	Holocene ..	1/50th	Wholly recent

26

highly revealing, especially those indestructible and extraordinarily idiosyncratic things, teeth. A whole skull is obviously a great find. In distinguishing mannish and apelike characteristics teeth, jaw, cranium (size and shape of brain), and the bones of hip and thigh— surprising, but we shall see the reason—are the discoveries most helpful in building up the story of our probable ancestry.

Let us, quite shortly and without too deeply weighing the argu-

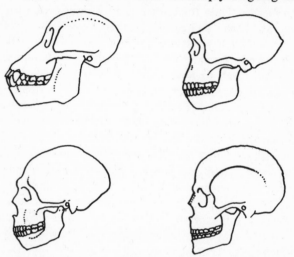

Here, reading from left to right and for comparison, are the skulls of Proconsul, Pithecanthropus, Neanderthal Man and *Homo sapiens*. (If drawn to scale, the first would be considerably and the second a little smaller)

ments, tell this story as at present believed and as based on the table given on page 25.*

Man's 'common inheritance' you will recall is the vertebrate ground-plan of head, and brain-case, and backbone with four digeted appendages or limbs hooked symmetrically thereon. His characteristics of 'independent acquisition' on the other hand are an

* Here are a few suggested books for those who wish to follow the argument. (*These and all future references to books are numbered and, with details of publication, shown under the title 'Further Reading' at the end of the book.*) First, *History of the Primates*[1] by W. E. Le Gros Clark, together with the reprint of one of his lectures on the subject appearing in *Discovery* of January 1955. Also *Meeting Prehistoric Man*[2] by G. H. R. von Koenigswald, *Early Man*[3] by A. H. Brodrick, *The Prehistory of East Africa*[4] by Sonia Cole, *Man the Toolmaker*[5] by K. P. Oakley, and *Man in Search of His Ancestors*[6] by André Senet.

upright stance, a jaw that enables him to talk, and a very large and convoluted brain particularly developed in its fore part. The modern anthropoid ape has gone in for tusk-like canine teeth, a jaw powerful to bite and not to talk, and limbs specialized for swinging skilfully (called 'brachiating') in the trees. If there is a common ancestor to the two it will be sufficiently generalized to show the *possibility* for its descendants to follow either of those paths.

Parapithecus ('Near to Ape') and Proconsul (given for once a nickname rather than a Greek name, there being a famous Zoo ape at that time called Consul) are the creatures discovered that most nearly fill the bill. Actually they fill it pretty well. *Parapithecus* has teeth that show him to have been a very primitive and probably 'generalized' or unspecialized creature; he was the size of a small monkey, and had some relationship to the tarsier (another of the Primates, whose significance we shall discover when we come to examine man's inheritance on the rather less material plane). Proconsul was a type rather than a single creature, ranging in size from gibbon to gorilla. Small and primitive and unspecialized ape had not only grown but increased; had in fact done so enormously, enjoying in what seems to have been the forcing ground of East Africa the sort of explosive burst of evolution that sometimes occurs and that may even have happened again with man himself and in much the same area. Proconsul was not very big-brained. But though comparable with modern apes in size he differed from them considerably. He had no 'simian shelf', a massive strengthening of the lower jaw, and his teeth fitted into his head more in the way that ours now fit. Of greatest significance, his limb bones were slender, though his arms were not over-long: a nimble but not a brachiating creature.

He and his like during Miocene and Pliocene times spread over Africa and Europe and Asia, changing and evolving slowly. A recognized type, Dryopithecus, Ape of the Trees, is found in Europe and India. He remains a lightly built and agile but non-brachiating animal; his canine tooth is more of a fang than ours, but his molars have something in common with early man's. He could very well be the father of modern apes; he could almost as well be the father of man.

Now we come to the gap, and after it to two sets of discoveries, both comparatively recent, that are far the most important in the story—indeed without them there would hardly be a coherent story of man's origins at all. They are *Australopithecus africanus* or

Southern Ape of Africa and *Pithecanthropus* or Ape-Man, found originally in Java and in the caves of Choukoutien near Pekin.

We could go into detail again about teeth and jaw and so forth; but there is one fact of such overwhelming importance that it swamps the rest and we can concentrate on that. *Here have been discovered live creatures that walked upright.* The shape of femur and particularly of pelvis, so different from those of modern anthropoid apes, shows this most clearly. Here is no brachiating early chimpanzee but ground-walking pre-*man*.

The other most important characteristic is the size of the brain (not of course the only criterion of intelligence but a good rough guide). The average capacity in cubic centimetres of the brain-cases of modern ape, Australopithecus, Pithecanthropus and *Homo sapiens* are respectively: 500; 600; 900; 1,350. This brings out two important and different points: firstly, these discovered creatures have already surpassed the apes; secondly, there is however a long way yet to go. Our ancestors in fact seem to have arrived at a form and gait and appearance recognizably like our own before they had anywhere nearly acquired our brain—a conclusion the opposite incidentally from that to be derived from the Piltdown fake, which was modern human skull and orang-utan's or chimpanzee's jaw—a poor 'Dawn Man' whose sun has now for ever set.

It will be noticed that one of these creatures of half a million years ago has 'ape' alone in its latinized Greek name and the other has both 'ape' and 'man'. That distinction can lead and has led to interminable argument and misunderstanding, and if we are going to avoid that sort of thing here we must agree upon a definition. By 'man' we obviously do not mean only *Homo sapiens*; there must have been many species of men though only one finally survived. The question is, what is to be the criterion of human status? The answer, the only reasonable answer that is now generally accepted, is: someone who was *capable of using tools*. Here is an ability that separates its owner from the rest of the animal kingdom and admits him across the threshold. Pithecanthropus passes the test: he had quartz tools, not very good but then quartz is a difficult medium. Australopithecus only *may* have used flint tools: possibly we are being unfair to him, but on present evidence we cannot let him in. As for the title *pithecus*, it is deserved because both creatures were by our standards ape-like; but since the word makes us think inescapably of the modern

THE STORY OF MAN

anthropoid apes it is an unfortunate title. In this book the Austra-
lopithecines will be called 'half men'—they were obviously nearer to
ourselves than any creature now alive—and Pithecanthropus and all
that follow him will be called, simply, 'man'.

The next to follow in our list is Heidelberg Man. He is now regarded as probably on a level with Pithecanthropus, either a parallel
development or the same species migrated into Europe.

From now on, the tools of man as well as his bones become
evidence. Indeed the tools—of flint principally, which are indestructible—are the much more frequent discoveries. As anthropologists
dug it became increasingly obvious that over thousands upon
thousands of years a tool of a standard and virtually unchanging
pattern—more of this in a later chapter—was being used in Europe
and Africa and Asia; but nowhere were the bones of its user being
discovered. The next on our list, Atlanthropus, is included because
with him bones and tools of this kind were at last found together—
and behold, Atlanthropus proved hardly distinguishable from the
Man of Pekin and the Man of Heidelberg, he being in fact another
Pithecanthropus. Both progress and change are still moving very,
very slowly.

But then comes a speeding up. The evidence also becomes prolific—Kenneth Oakley for instance in his book *Man the Toolmaker*
lists no less than sixteen different finds between Atlanthropus and
true and undoubted *Homo sapiens*. Here we have obviously had to be
highly selective in our listing—we also have to do some pretty wide
generalizings to achieve any clear picture at all. In essence the story
that the fossils and the flints now tell us is this: after, and probably
out of, Pithecanthropus, the first of the upright walkers who undoubtedly used tools, there developed finally a type now called the
'generalized Neanderthal type'; and from him there sprang *two*
branches, an 'extreme' Neanderthaler and—at last we reach haven!
—*Homo sapiens*.

The Neanderthaler—the man first found in the 'thal' or dale of
Neander near Dusseldorf—is of course famous; he is the original
brutish Cave Man, usually depicted brandishing a club. We shall do
well to forget most of that picture, though he probably was brutal
to look at. He was not in his 'extreme' form our ancestor; in his
generalized form the chances are that he was.

Another German find, the Steinheim skull, is as good as any as a specimen of the generalized Neanderthaler, and he therefore comes next on our list. He was an improvement on Pithecanthropus in that his brain size had increased by 100 c.c. or so and a good deal of that increase seems to have been at the front, where it was needed—he was not so low-browed. Nor was either the jaw or the overhanging ridge at the level of the eyebrows—a typical simian feature—so prominent.

Then a curious thing seems to have happened. The two divergent lines both rapidly developed their brains, the 'extreme' Neanderthaler even developing slightly the bigger. But in all other respects the extreme type lost the race. He became not less ape-like but more; he retrogressed. He is an interesting and rather pathetic figure, and we shall have a good deal more later to say about him.

The other line, through the Steinheim skull, leads at last to *Homo sapiens* in the role of Aurignacian Man. He turns up, perfect, perhaps even a little superior to ourselves, in the caves of France, and is there dated as having lived some twenty or so thousand years ago. That is a long time historically but a mere moment evolutionarily, a flick of the eyelid of God. One thing must be made finally clear. Aurignacian Man 'turns up' in Southern France: he must have developed elsewhere. The exact age of *Homo sapiens* is unknown and under hot dispute. There is the Swanscombe skull for instance, found in Kent; that might date our species as already in existence as much as two hundred thousand years ago. But neither is the date at all well established nor, since the find is hardly a skull but only two large bits of one with no face or jaw, is the type of man represented at all certain. Anthropolgists are inclined to seize on *possibilities* as to the age of *Homo sapiens* to suit their book, and to proceed to build rather tall theories on the wobbly foundation. As far as this book is concerned however—and I think this may be legitimately stressed—these arguments do not matter very much. Indeed they hardly matter at all. At some time or another *Homo sapiens* came, and with him and for a long time before him came other men very like him. Whether we have or have not the blood of those others in our veins we are nevertheless heir to their traditions, their culture and their way of thinking. Those are the things that matter.

Note: The Leakeys' recent discovery of the "Olduvai skull" in Tanganyika increases the claim of Australopithicus to be a true man rather than a half man.

2

Towards Sensitivity

W E HAVE established, dissolving rather than suppressing any lingering doubts, that man is a creation not separate from but evolving out of the animal kingdom.

He is also a unique and supremely different animal. He takes certain mental and spiritual characteristics of the beasts, capabilities that are discernible but no more than discernible, and enlarges them out of all recognition. He has sensitivity; he has understanding; he has imagination and is capable of deep and impassioned emotion. He outstrips the rest of creation as did the forms of life that crawled out of their original watery home outstrip the life that it left behind, as, in a more modern idiom, a jet outstrips a piston-engined aeroplane. With new powers he is going to do what no other animal has done before him: control his environment and not merely adapt himself to it. Before we watch him beginning to do this we shall in this and the two following chapters enquire into the ways in which he acquired his powers. We must do that if we are to understand. For man-from-animal is an entirely different creature from that hypothetical entity that has nevertheless been unanimously assumed until recently to have existed: man, creation *de novo*. We shall be spanning Evolution in dizzy jumps; and it will not be entirely mental processes that we shall be watching, body skills and body urges being inseparable from the activities of the brain.

Even the humble animalcule—the lowly 'first life', *protozoon*—possesses what has been called 'irritability', the power of being excited to action by a physical stimulus: it shuns for instance too bright a light or an unusual chemical constituency of the water it lives in; it is prodded into its primitive methods of ingestion when it meets what it recognizes as food.

When life takes the next great step, from a single cell to a colony of cells, several things happen. Specialization appears, with some cells responsible for the birth of the next generation and others beginning to refine mere irritability at too bright a light into a sensitivity to it, possessing for the purpose a 'red spot' that is the very beginning of vision. But with cells starting to specialize there must also come co-ordination and control. That round green pinhead of life, Volvox—whether you call it animal or vegetable is hardly material—sees to it that its little lashing oars of cilia all work the same way. Hit a sponge in one place, and that place, like some incredibly doped boxer, will slowly cover up to protect itself.

In fact a message has been carried in some way from cell to cell. The logical improvement to this, as it is the actual, is for one type of cell to specialize in message carrying and to elongate itself from a blob to a very long thread. This, the *nerve*, is one of the greatest inventions of life. Embodiment of sensitivity and directiveness, it will convey messages both of feeling from the outside world and of command to action in response.

But then what does the commanding? A mere nerve network evolves into a nerve system, with as its hub a ganglion that is best though no doubt not wholly accurately comparable to a telephone exchange. The jellyfish, knowing where is light and where is darkness, which is up and which is down, flaps its way to the surface so that it may sink slowly and catch whatever is edible on the way. It is acting like a co-ordinated animal, in that it is not merely meeting but searching for its food. Planaria, a little arrow-shaped flatworm, does better.

Planaria does better because it possesses three things: a body pattern that gives it a front and a back end, the power to move forward in the direction of the front end, and a nerve ganglion at the front that tells it where to go. So life, in the shallow waters of the distant Paleozoic world and in the shape of the first flatworm, has invented *the head*. It has invented too—to continue this tremendous simplification of the evolutionary story—what the modern cybernetic* engineer calls 'feed back': the sensitive thing-in-front feeds messages back to the body behind, there to excite or inhibit action. This thing, though hardly worthy of the name as yet, is going to become the brain.

* From the Greek for a steersman; the science of automatic control.

But what is the matter with the flatworm is its flatness. The animal is nearly all surface, hardly more than two-dimensional: it is such a simple creature that all it needs in order to oxygenate itself and so extract energy from its food is a surface in contact with the surrounding water. Flesh, if it is going to be properly three-dimensional, if it is going to have bulk, must be served by that other entity that in popular speech goes so significantly with it, *blood*—'the blood that is the life thereof', the carrier of oxygen and food (and in the higher forms of life a great deal else) around the body. There arrive the round and the segmented worms, plainly three-dimensional, pushing around their blood by rhythmic pulsations of their body. From that simple method will evolve the specialist organ for the same purpose, the heart.

There then followed—after due lapse of millions of years—two

'Feed-back': life with a head. (Marine worm, which has not changed much since he began in the Paleozoic Era)

utterly divergent patterns of body that were finally to develop two also utterly divergent patterns of mind: the arthropod and the vertebrate.

But remember that all life is as yet still confined to the waters, has not climbed out on to the dry land. It is doing pretty well: it has developed sex to help it play more varied tunes on the intricate keyboard of heredity, and increased its sensitivities to the pressures and chemical constituencies of the waters it lives in; it is developing feelers for touch and taste, and eyes with which, rather dimly, to see. The arthropod, the jointed-limbed, arrives first, to be also the first of the animals to crawl out of the water, to form thereafter the arachnids and the insects. The vertebrate, the backboned animal, coming later, first develops its success in the rivers and the sea.

The fish, the earliest true vertebrate, perfects as it were the front-and-back-end pattern of life. It becomes neat and streamlined and, with its tail and its fins, a beautiful expositor of controlled speed within the water. The fish takes a long time to do this, it experiments with fantastic forms while plant life and jointed life is already experimenting on land; but it does it in the end. And of course it does something much more, something that every school-boy reader about *coelocanth* knows. Some kind of fish or other turned its stumpy lobes of fins into rudimentary legs and itself into an amphibian. . . .

Amphibian—*amphi bios*—double life. The duplication is between land and water: not yet is life wholly terrestrial. The new lumbering, crawling, wallowing form of life, large-snouted fish-on-legs, will be born in water, will never go far from water lest his skin dry out, will return—like many of his contemporaries in the insect world—to the water when the urge comes to propagate the next generation of his kind.

Next, and with the reptile, comes the complete emancipation from the water. The instruments that achieve the change are a skin that can withstand the heat of the sun and, in particular, a new way of giving birth to the next generation. So far the waters themselves, with their buoyancy and their movement, have been the means of bringing together the seed of the male and the seed of the female. Now, to solve the new problem what we call internal fertilization will be evolved and the female will cease merely to spawn and will learn to produce the protected, the already father-and-food-pro-vided, egg.

That single change has tremendous implications for the way of life of the new sorts of creatures that have come to inhabit this earth. But these are really only part of larger implications resulting from the very fact of being emancipated from the water. It is not an easy or only pleasant emancipation; indeed it must in some ways have been more in the nature of a shock. The extremes of heat and cold to be met are now vastly greater. There is the darkness of the night and the brilliance of the day—the heat of the sun to fear and the 'furious winter's rages'. There is the sharpness of the rocks and the bitterness of the wind. And yet all this is of course a challenge and an opportunity as well as a threat and shock. Air is clearer than water; it carries scent better and sound better. Sight can and does improve; scent grows keener; true hearing is born. And not only does hearing arrive but something to hear: at last the world is no longer silent but for the crash of the waterfall or the fallen tree or

35

the clap of thunder. The male has now to find the female: in the significant if sentimental phrases, life 'calls to its mate'. With the reptile life begins to become recognizably like our own; these land creatures we can believe in as our ancestors.

And yet only just can we so believe, and very curiously do the reptiles seem to react to their opportunities. Alas they had no brain.

At least very nearly they had no brain. They had brawn instead. Some of the larger needed a secondary nerve control, a 'deputy brain', halfway down their spine, something that must have been purely automatic in its reactions, as unconscious as that part of our own brain that controls our breathing or our balance. This is amazing and has led to endless jokes, such as that one could bite off the tail of a slow-witted saurian and 'get away with it'. All this is not a retrogression however. Nothing in the sea had as yet done very much better. And it is a fact, perhaps a salutary fact, that the reptiles did flourish greatly, not only conquering the land, but following the insects into the air and returning in many specially adapted forms to the sea. On land many of them did something the amphibians never seem to have managed properly: they changed their legs into real pillars of support and lifted their bellies off the ground. Some went further and, like man, raised themselves up on to their hind legs. They failed signally however to make anything much out of their forelimbs: you do need a brain to thread a needle or even pick and peel a fruit. Nor of course were all the prehistoric reptiles giants; some of the smaller must really have been quick and active, running on their long back legs as the frilled lizard does today or the chicken crossing the road.

But not *always* active. There was something the matter with the reptiles, as there was with the flatworm. They had blood indeed; but it was 'cold'.

The commonly accepted overtones and simplifications of that adjective need not be discounted. With warm-bloodedness does go increased sensitivity, and responsiveness, and capacity for the emotions, though it is not all necessarily a matter of cause and effect. There are however some pretty obvious disadvantages in having a body whose temperature cannot be kept constant but varies with the heat and cold that lies around. The most obvious is that if the weather freezes you freeze too—unless you can take some sort of avoiding action, and that may not be possible. The less obvious disadvantage is that with a drop in temperature your metabolism and your nervous reactions work more slowly, and conversely any burst of energy will so heat your body that you will fairly soon have to desist. The reptile may love the sun, as the motorist may be glad of his insurance policy or the tightrope walker his balancing stick. But it will not be all beneficence. Watch a reptile. It will be most of the time horribly lethargic, preternaturally still. It will never *fidget*, which may seem an advantage; but he has none of the nervous abilities that go with the power to fidget. . . .

The next great step is known to everyone: the entrance of the mammal.

Actually there are two great steps, very near together in geological time, the creation of the bird and the creation of the mammal. Both patterns of life must undoubtedly have been evolved from the reptile—from the super-pattern, that is to say, that is by now firmly established as successful, the limbed vertebrate. The birds are different from us essentially not in their pattern of body but in their pattern of mind, as indeed even more startlingly different are the insects: that is an aspect we shall need to look at again later. Now we will follow the line of fur not feathers.

The idea that man belongs to the furred animals will I hope worry no one nowadays, nor for that matter the fact that he has largely lost his fur. How much this is a result of wearing clothes it is not easy to tell, though rather obviously not very much: though a great initial help to warm-bloodedness it is not, curiously enough, a necessity. What is fundamental is that man is a mammal and shares with most of his cousins these four great advantages:

> Thermostasis
> Viviparity
> Mammae
> Placenta

That is scientific language that needs bringing to life. It is not difficult.

Thermostasis is the keeping of the body at an even temperature, is warm-bloodedness. It sweeps away the disadvantages of the momentarily frenzied, usually lethargic and always cold-fearing reptile. It does more. Warm skin, and the fur or hair that goes with it, are most pleasant to the senses, of touch and smell not least—if we don't mention these things in polite society we are not at present thinking in terms of polite society. To be viviparous, to give live birth, is not alone the property of the mammal. But when it is coupled with the possession of mammae, the giving of suck, something entirely new arrives—and something intensely intimate. All life has a passion—a mindless passion perhaps, but still a passion—for producing and protecting the next generation. In insects, in many lower forms of life, it may lead, even in the act of procreation, to the loss of the parent's life. It is all, essentially, terribly impersonal. But with the creature who stays with and feeds her young the position is entirely different. Here the birds and the mammals have made a great advance. It is something in which all the benefits of warm-bloodedness combine—and something which, for the reason that sentimental and not scientific language has to be used, is I think much too greatly discounted. The advance I refer to is the birth of true love. Let us not jib at that phrase, but try at the same time to divorce it from too much sentimentality. Not only mother love is meant here but sexual love: a compound of intimate sensualities, lickings, smellings, touchings, fondlings, caressings; and gradually evolving, with the growth of brain and imagination, into something more spiritual. Does the kangaroo love her young? Probably, though hardly when there is born that amorphous, infinitesimal embodiment of no more than an instinct and ability to climb to and fasten on to a teat. We must not in fact leave out in our generalizations the importance of the placenta, which makes the foetus literally blood of its mother's blood and enables there to be born in miniature perfection a body-machine of the most beautiful and subtle intricacy—and something incidentally that the mother finds much more satisfactory than any machine.

Now we will drop a little from this high plane. The mammal, once it had established itself, had all the advantages; but it was, from the point of view of our hind-sight, a little slow to use them. It burst forth first of all, as had the reptile before it, into giantism. This seems a habit of life when it meets and takes a new opportunity, a sort of exaggerated exuberance.* There is of course an obvious and immediate benefit in bigness: it gives its owner, if other things are equal, an advantage in the fierce struggle for existence. In a big creature too the ratio of surface to bulk is less, and to a creature that possesses the ability to keep warm and alive in a cold climate this is a consideration: the rate of living, of heart-beat and of having to fill one's belly, is in such little creatures as the mouse and the mole and the shrew fantastically high. Yet, what is important to

Mere bulk that failed. Baluchithere, who browsed 20 feet up and
lived fifty million years ago. He didn't survive

realize, mere bulk without brain does *not* succeed—witness the fact that mouse and mole and shrew are still with us, while Eobasilius and Baluchitherium and all the rest of the pathetic army of early galumphers have gone permanently from the face of the earth.

Brain with these early mammalian giants had not increased to any really great extent above the low level of the reptiles. Then as the Eocene Period faded out into the Oligocene and so into the Miocene the thing happened. There came an, as it were, second and

* There is some evidence for this having happened with the *hominidae*, the family of man; though *Gigantopithecus* is much too questionably our ancestor to appear in the chart.

improved issue of mammals, the kinds that were mostly still alive when man, the genus *Homo*, came upon the scene.

We have reached, physically, the last lap. The second army of mammals filled the earth most successfully and with a fresh access of evolutionary exuberance. But these new and bigger-brained mammals, heirs as one might say to a magnificent constitution, a most efficient bodily instrument, met their environment, as had the reptiles before them, *in detail*. They deployed over the face of the earth and they adapted themselves to its great variety of environment: some with long legs for the new grassy plains; some, in a sort of cowardly infantilism, with tail or flippers back to the nursery sea; some to the trees of the forest, to the swamp, to below the earth, to the inviting, insect-ridden air. And with each adaptation to a particular environment went some sacrifice of the essential vertebrate birthright. The man-beast, the hominid, then came upon the scene, and he had not sacrificed so much. Only essentially one thing, in fact: offensive or defensive weapons, having neither great strength nor weight nor speed, neither rending claws nor ravenous jaws. What was evolved for him in their place will constitute the next chapter.

3

Towards Understanding

T O RECAPITULATE, we are tracing, very rapidly, the course
of evolution that led up to ourselves: man's legacy from the
beasts. We are working on the theory that this is a matter of
increasing sensitivity, awareness and successful response to environment. We have reached as far as the mammals and to that kind of
mammal that did *not* specialize elaborately.

Perhaps we need a word of defence against a suspicion that we
are being altogether too complacent. Evolution does not lead automatically up and up and on and on until it culminates in that
miracle, man. It has led there. But it has led to many other places
as well, not half so admirable. Life, essentially, takes its opportunity,
fits itself; and it does so with an exactitude, a variety and an ingenuity
that is indeed miraculous and can be given any epithet of wonder
and admiration that anyone likes to invent. But this magnificent
drive that seems to lie behind life does not necessarily lead anywhere; in fact the more meticulous the adaptation the less it will
lead anywhere, except to the grave. Life that adapts itself too exactly
will either die out if the environment should considerably change or
stay immutable should it find an environment that stays put with it.
The life that led to man did not do that. Man cannot take the credit;
if he does not wish he need not even attribute any design to the
events that led to himself. But at least there is no necessity to feel
apologetic for recounting a success story when that story exists—
as it undoubtedly does, however doubtful we may now feel about
our capacity to continue it to a happy conclusion. Now we will
proceed.

Eye, hand and brain is the theme. It is one that has been repeated
often, perhaps unquestioningly, but it is reasonable and likely to be
true. Let it be remembered however that no one can trace this story

41

of the rise of the Primates and their brain power with complete certainty.

The Primates are the family of mammals that it is believed led to man and that includes besides ourselves the following living creatures:

> Tree Shrew
> Lemur
> Spectral Tarsier
> Monkey
> Anthropoid Ape

Those are anatomically our nearest relatives. In all instances fossil equivalents, rather less specialized, possessing fewer characteristics of 'independent acquisition', have been discovered.

Tree shrew is small and ancient in lineage. He is whiskered and snouted and superficially squirrel-like and he probably evolved from an insect eater. His paws with which he clings to the branches are, though fitted with claws, very like hands; and his ears are in shape curiously human. His kind is found very early in the record of the mammals—perhaps his direct progenitors were keeping out of the way and successfully evolving while the giant reptiles were suffering the whips and scorns of time and sliding to their death. The tree shrew is not a nocturnal animal, and he is very quick and active. A late kind of fossil tree shrew must have had flat nails instead of claws and was more like a lemur.

Fossil lemurs abound. They must have been prolific; some by the standard of the modern remnant were huge. The modern lemurs —they include the potto and galago, two delightful and friendly little creatures—are agile climbers and (galago) clever jumpers. They are wet-muzzled like a dog but not so snouted as the tree shrew, and their eyes are both nearer to the front and bigger. Their paws are recognizably hands and they have left themselves only one digit with a claw—with which they scratch.

Tarsiers, like lemurs, once existed in great variety. They are so very transitional anatomically that it is difficult sometimes to know where to classify them. Of the one extant species of tarsier it is enough to say that he is the size only of a rather scraggy two-week-old kitten but can jump accurately to a distance of six feet, and that he has more of a mouth than a muzzle and two forward-looking eyes that are startlingly enormous.

Monkeys were and are in great variety. Those of the Old World have no tail that can be used to help balance or cling. For the rest I suggest that you call to mind any watching you may have done of a monkey at the Zoo, for preference perhaps a baby rhesus monkey

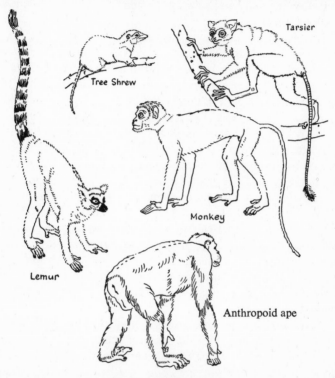

The five other Primates.

whose shape and set of head is so like a human baby's. Questing snout and wet-nosed muzzle have completely gone. Instead there is— a face. Eyes and lips are mobile; there is expression and changing expression at that. Then there are hands, real and unquestionable, and they are very active hands, imitative, and supremely inquisitive.

As for the anthropoid ape, modern forms are too specialized for them to have much significance for us. The fossil apes are mostly, as we said of the specimens listed in Chapter 1, light of limb—creatures as agile perhaps as the modern gibbon but without his absurdly exaggerated trapeze-artist arms. Two things we can say in generalization about them, whether modern or ancient: they have lost their tails, and they have won pretty sizeable brains.

Now let us see what all this means in terms of that upward course of sensitivity and successful commerce with the environment that led to man.

The mammal, so long as he stayed on the ground, was the supreme *smeller*—significant maker and subtle appreciator of smells. Surprisingly, this sense that had come in a dim form out of the water and that still needed dampness for it to function was made by the supreme land animal (as it was indeed by many aerial insects but not by the bird) into the chief instrument for awareness of the outside world. Smell has of course its advantages; it is all-pervading, it gets as one may say, round corners, which is certainly more than sight does. But it has little else to recommend it. The creature who, with nose to the ground, seeks satisfaction and avoids danger in this way, will not obtain a very vivid or stimulating conception of his world. He will not lift his eyes unto the hills or even to the trees or for that matter to anything that cannot have sniffed up from it the tell-tale molecules: dogs may, as G. K. Chesterton suggests, love the brave smell of a stone but what they love better is the keen smell of the creature that has last touched it. Smell is not in the least an impersonal or objective sense, nor stimulating to anything but the most elemental reactions.

Successful life in the trees seems to need and stimulate good sight and to do the reverse with the sense of smell; this is a reasonable supposition since scent carries and can be followed more effectively on the ground, and if you are going to move about the trees with speed and certainty you will obviously need to know everything that good sight can tell you about the place where you intend to land at the end of the jump.

It is of course much more than that. You need visual judgement. The evolutionary story of the Primates, all largely tree-dwellers, is in essence that one thing, a recession of the sense of smell and an advance of the powers of vision. The snout recedes, the eyes come to the front; the eyes develop the 'yellow spot' that gives powers of particularly concentrated vision at will, they above all achieve stereoscopic vision or power to see in the round. That improves judgement of distance out of hand.

It does more. It enables its fortunate owner to appreciate the texture and the shape of things. With that sort of eye and no longer that sort of snout one can *examine* things. One can do so, that is to say, if one can pick them up. That is where hands come in—hands that having learnt to grasp the bough can now grasp what they will.

And thirdly and of course from these: the brain. You can't examine without brain.

Nor for that matter can you precisely jump and balance without brain. The brain is a great instrument. It is the servant of the senses and the master of the body; it receives all the varied impressions from the environment, sorts them, considers them and sends out the required responses to the body and the limbs. So there in fact is the trilogy, eye, hand and brains; and the true story can be nothing else than that the three through the millenia worked for the benefit of the line of man in fruitful conjunction, each stimulating the growth and increasingly subtle improvement of the other two. Eye had to be good if hand was going to be useful; brain had to be more efficient at interpretation if it was going to keep up with eye; hand could be even cleverer now that it had a better brain to direct it. Life, you will remember, takes its opportunity, whether in good mood or bad, whether set on settling more comfortably in somebody's else guts, or on inventing the differential calculus. Here it was in good mood. . . .

But what a long way yet from the differential calculus! If the story of the evolution of the progenitors of man is the story of the development in a single line of mammals of eye, hand and brain, then the greatest of these without any shadow of doubt is brain. The development of brain overshadows everything else. When the genus *Homo* arrived upon the earth the brain had still a long way to go; nevertheless even before crossing that threshold life had evolved something very wonderful and quite unique. We must in the rest of this chapter look pretty closely at the growth of brain and get some idea of how this supreme instrument works. The brain does a number of things quite lowly as well as exalted; it is Protean and might be given half a dozen names as justifiably as one; it is as versatile as a music hall artist—a good one, that is—as well as being as august as Caesar, unpredictable as Cleopatra. We must consider it circumspectly and with respect.

Before doing so however there is necessary one word of warning lest what has gone so far in this chapter should give the wrong impression. We have passed in rapid review the existing Primates and their fossil equivalents. But nobody knows for certain the true ancestry of man. Nobody ever will, for the simple reason that man was not there to observe it. This is no doubt a pity, and tantalizing; but it is no tremendous loss. The details do not matter very much, as long as we are reasonably sure of the outline. And of that I think we can be sure. The geologist, the anatomist, the paleontologist: if they have not always worked together as they might have done, they have by now collected an enormous amount of evidence and do between them give us a pretty clear picture. Man came from an un-specialized line of mammals that by living in the trees developed in a way that made a final phenomenal burst of brain-power possible. Man did *not* come from an animal that looked like any of the present so-called anthropoid apes nor probably very like any of the present monkeys; there is no grand automatically ascending line 'from the monkeys to ourselves'. That needs stressing, however much we may persuade ourselves that we are nowadays too in-telligent and knowledgeable to need the warning; for it is what we were once taught.

Now back to the brain. If successful evolution is for some in-dividual emanation of life to win better dominance over its environ-ment, then that individual must be a well-integrated whole, must have the greatest possible functional solidarity. That is the brain's job: to weld (to quote the *Encyclopaedia Britannica*) 'the body's component parts into one consolidated mechanism facing as a united entity the changeful world about it'. A big job indeed.

The body itself has to be regulated, and the more complicated the body the bigger the job. Breathing must be kept going; with a warm-blooded creature temperature must be adjusted automatically to varying conditions; hunger and thirst must be registered. From outside the warning message of pain must be registered; the senses —smell, taste, touch, hearing, sight—must, alone or in combination, be attended to. Then, in response, the commands must go out to the hormones, the glands, the nerves, the muscles.

A great deal of this does not involve our *conscious* brain. That does not lessen its importance. But what matters for real command

46

over the environment is conscious response. This is where this business of smell comes into the picture again.

It comes in as the developing and dominant sense as life climbed out of the waters and began to take command of the land. What was wanted, with the delicate air blowing so subtly where it listed and the dangers and delights of a terrestrial existence making themselves apparent, was obviously something better than a so-called brain that said, 'Smell—good—go on!' or 'Smell—bad—stop!' What was wanted was an instrument that said, 'I remember this smell; it is so-and-so, and the way to catch it, or avoid it, is such-and-such.' There developed what has been called a 'fore-brain'; and with the

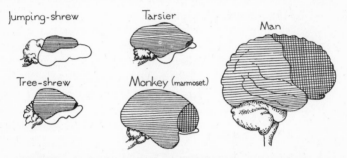

Mammalian brains in the line that probably led to man. Unshaded, *archipallium*. Shaded, *neopallium*. Double shaded, *frontal area*

early types of land vertebrates it is so much one thing only that it is also called in their case the 'smell brain'.

But the snout, the front-end-that-meets-things, grew sensitive to touch as well as to smell, a reasonably obvious development. There grew in the fore-brain therefore an area sensitive to, responsible for, touch. It considered touch, as the rest of the fore-brain considered smell. Not only that but it considered the two *together*.

From that really came all that is marvellous and exceptional in the brain of man: it is the beginning of the brain as an efficient *blender* of experience. So much is this a new and promising development that the brain with this new function is given a new name, *neo* (new) *pallium*, as opposed to *archipallium* (old). Pallium is from the Latin for cloak, because this fore-brain has spread out in the top and front of the head and is covering or cloaking the more primitive parts of half-conscious or unconscious controls and reactions. Not only that but the new is as it were more of a pallium than the old: it mounts, and spreads, and overlays—'a tide of grey matter'.

Here fits in what has been said of the educating power of tree-life for the Primates. Primate brain, as we know it from living examples and from the size, shape and internal markings of the fossil skulls, shows a steady and remarkable shrinkage of the smell centre of the fore-brain and an increase in the centres of hearing and, in particular, of touch and sight. As the hands took over sensitivity from the snout, as the eyes took over from the nose, and as both learnt to do so much more and to make demands for more subtle control and discrimination in the brain, so the brain physically grew and changed. In man the smell centre, the 'olfactory lobe', is completely overlaid by the cerebral hemispheres.

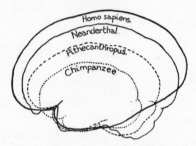

The swelling and overtoppling brain

And that is the final stage in the evolution of the brain as the Primate stock moves towards man. The cerebral hemispheres are formed: that is to say the pallium, the spreading cloak, already divided and cleft down the middle, spreads even further and, to make more room for itself and more surface, bends and buckles to form a convoluted cortex or 'rind'. That rind, if smoothed out flat, would cover the amazingly large area of two square feet, or about three times the size of the double page that you are reading.

Not only that but there develops in the fore-brain a part as it were even more 'fore', both in physical position and in function. This is the *frontal area* or sometimes called the silent area, silent because in experiments on the brain it gives no response to any of the sensory nerves. That really gives it its pre-eminence. It receives no direct messages; it is a super co-ordinator, a blender-in-chief, a *considerer*. It is indeed something of a miracle, the most complicated

48

piece of life ever created, something that man cannot as yet much explain physically. It is the organ that forms associations, remembers and compares, cogitates, considers, worries, worries-out. We could probably exist without it, we might even be happier without it; but there would be no Napoleons, no Shakespeares, no Beethovens, no Rutherfords, perhaps even no mute inglorious Miltons using their powers of imagination and philosophy in the quiet village lower planes of thought. . . .

All that is a terribly broad generalization, for the brain is a very complicated instrument, one that is difficult to experiment upon and learn about and that does not fit exact descriptions. For instance it is not only that as we go up the Primate ladder fore-brain spreads and overshadows the rest; it also takes over functions from the rest, so that many that are performed by lower animals simply or half consciously are now performed better and more subtly and more consciously.

It is a most remarkable story of an outstanding advance. Perhaps however 'growth' is a better word. That I think is the thing to remember at the end of this chapter. The brain that appeared when man appeared was indeed something new; but it was not in the least something wholly new. It had evolved. All the back parts, the old parts, though overshadowed and robbed of their higher functions— robbed as the bright boy of the class robs the dunce of his pen or protractor to make better use of it, as David robbed Uriah of Bathsheba to make her a queen—all is very much *still there*. If a bad joke will make a good mnemonic: we inherit not the Old Adam but the Old Archy Pallium.

4

Deep Feeling

THOUGH in unscientific language we may use words loosely
yet we also use them with such metaphorical overtones that
they have a forcefulness they could not otherwise possess.
Such a word is 'feeling' used in all other senses than the physical.
There is no word that we can substitute for it; 'emotion' is perhaps
the nearest.

I believe that if there is one thing outstanding about primitive
man that is liable to be insufficiently appreciated it is his capacity for
feeling. Economic Man may have come to exist, the man whose
mainspring of conduct is the hard and careful assessment of material
advantage; but if he does exist then he is as it were no more than a
'pallium', an overlay covering rather inadequately and imperman-
ently a man much less reasonable, more unpredictable, and more
elemental. Primitive man is, and must surely have been at the beginning, as far from Economic Man as is fancy dress from prison
garb, as *vol-au-vent* from damper, or as a barmaid from a penny-in-
the-slot machine.

How on earth did man get his emotions? How for that matter did
animals get theirs? This is difficult. Is it a matter of brain?—for we
have said, and rightly, that brain is the outstanding possession of
man. The answer is, partly so, and a matter of the lower and evolutionarily older parts of the brain at that—though it would be a misleading over-simplification to think of man as in possession of a
new and reasoning brain continually at war with, continually trying
to control, an old and elemental one. We shall do better now to stop
thinking in terms of the physical brain. We shall do somewhat better
to think in terms of that once new but by now hoary concept of the
'body-mind', the idea that we are not two entities occasionally
influencing each other, but one interwoven entity made up of

flesh, blood, nerves, glands, cortex, chemical messengers and the rest, none of which could exist, let alone function, without the others.

The best terms in which to think however are of behaviour. Animals behave in this way and that way—and most peculiar some of the ways are—and man was and still is an animal. The Life Force—and I fail to see how we can get on without the use of this term, though we need not necessarily impute any conscious purpose to it—the Life Force has as its main job the continuance of creation, and varied creation at that. It has done the job, one might say, with a staggering exuberance. It invented sex for the purpose. It invented too what we can only call 'spare time and surplus energy'. The two together—and often they do go together—produced the emotions. Or if they didn't, they exercised them. If we follow the evolution of sex and of surplus energy we ought to gain a pretty useful conception of what is man's legacy so far as the functioning of his emotions is concerned. Life in its progress has 'felt' fairly deeply one way and another, and man's ways owe a good deal, to say the least, to what has gone before.

We need once more to go back to the beginning, or at least somewhere near the beginning. Simple one-celled life knows not sex. It perpetuates its kind, as we are well aware, by the simple and drastic method of splitting into two. Its time comes upon it; it is seized with tremendous activity; it forms finally a waist, and then splits, each half perfect and complete with a packet of inherited characteristics inside. Don't let us talk of an amoeba trembling with emotion; but do let us allow that those who have seen this essential activity under the microscope speak of it almost with awe: giving birth was surely from the beginning a crucial, in the true sense of the word a horrific, occasion.

Life next invented the colony of cells and the specialization of cells within that colony, so that there might arrive something entitled to the name of an individual. One particular kind of specialization looked after the continuing of the species; instead of the whole creature splitting and growing again, a small part did—it budded off. Then a new idea: two kinds of cell, one that grows, one that fertilizes; the *ovum* and the *sperm*, the ovum relatively large and passive, having within it the power to grow once it is triggered off into activity; the sperm, small and active, seeking the ovum, finding and burrowing into it, not only releasing the trigger action but itself contributing to the newly started life.

Life, remember, is as yet only in the waters. That makes things simple and easy. Pour the ova into the surrounding element, equip the sperm with a whip-lash tail for swiming (it still has it) and pour it too; and some at least of the two will meet. Sex has arrived.

But it is hardly yet sex as we know it. Nature seemed at first fairly indifferent as to whether it grew the two kinds of sex cells in one individual or in two, and the first of these methods was obviously the simpler. Nor did this necessarily annul the advantage of sex, which is to multiply the variety of life, to introduce from two separate sources those 'mutations', those weals and scars that one might say are suffered by the germ plasm and that may by good fortune be beneficial to the new life in meeting and grabbing the advantage from a changed environment. Even when the animal is hermaphrodite, if more than two or three grow or come together and at a given signal pour out their sex cells into the moving waters, then cross-fertilization will happen and life will be served.

But what is the signal? There is amongst many of these lowly creatures today, and has no doubt always been, the power to pour into the waters 'secretions'—it is hardly the right word in this case, but no matter—in the same way as our endocrine glands pour secretions, the 'chemical messengers', into our blood. Here it is *ectocrine* instead of *endocrine*, outwards instead of inwards. That is the release that sets things going.

Now this is significant and interesting. We are moving towards courtship and love-making in animals, though we hardly realize it yet. Sponges sit and live near together and swop sex cells. Certain worms *come* together and do it. Ragworms change their appearance, swim to the surface, discharge their gonads, and die. The palolo worm does much the same; and its appointed time is so meticulously dictated by season and tide that other forms of life, man included, benefit from the exactness and dine off the worm. There is here something of the ruthlessness of sex as well as what might conceivably be called something of the beginnings of its romance.

Notice that it is always a matter of releasing, of triggering off: a process of timing, so that the biblical phrase 'her time came upon her'

52

is even already not entirely inappropriate. That is where courtship comes in. For courtship in its beginnings is no more than behaviour to set the processes of fertilization moving. It will become much more subtle and elaborate and beautiful than the crude casting of ecto-crines into the waters; but in essence it is the same thing. What is cheering, for ourselves that is to say who are the heir to all this, is how subtle and beautiful it does become—there is often a non-utilitarian excess about Nature that makes one almost like the harridan. Nor do we have to reach the stage beyond hermaphroditism before courtship—or at least sensuality and what must surely be the pleasures of sensuality—exist. Earthworms and snails are herm-aphrodite. But earthworms intertwine to exchange gonads, and garden snails stimulate each other by the caressing exchanges of slime and the prodding with small and specially grown calcerous spikes, which have been called by some rightly poetic naturalist 'love darts'.

As one would guess, the next step is the proper creation of the sexes, the one to carry the passive, but potentially powerful, ovum, the other the active and questing sperm. Impersonality in sex is now disappearing altogether, though behaviour will yet for a long time be instinctive rather than wholly on the conscious level. But that does not rule out emotion.

With the male it is largely the emotion of showing off. With the female it is largely reluctance, or perhaps rather passivity, a waiting and subconscious holding-back before being made to unfurl the surely highly star-spangled banner of emotions that must go with the drastic bodily processes that are in store for her.

That is the male's job: to excite the female—and himself in the process—in order that she may be induced, or triggered off (the word is still appropriate), to shed her spawn so that it may be over-laid with his milt. Colour, movement, dance, even ritual, all come into it, and this before life has wholly left the waters—arthropods and cephalapods, and big and little fish all do it, waving claws, swimming with splendid skill, taking on a brighter and more attrac-tive hue. It is a curious thing to have happened, a pleasant thing. The little estuarine fish are the best at it—they have need perhaps in their more changeful and dangerous environment to be the most in-telligent. The stickleback, as is well known, builds a nest, displays before his intended mate, nuzzles her forward into the home—and

53

later protects the ensuing young. And the fish, remember, though cold-blooded, is a vertebrate. . . .

Plants in Paleozoic times climbed out of the water, arthropods followed, vertebrates followed—and sex did not remain behind. The plant by devious routes evolved the flower, the pollen and the pistil and the stamen—one writer has called that an orgy of sex, but there is no emotion evolved so far as anyone can see, and we will therefore dismiss them. The arthropods evolved into (amongst other things) the insects and found sex a bully and even an executioner, but with what emotions for the individual it is hard to say. The vertebrate produced amphibian, reptile, bird, mammal in that order —and that is where our interest lies.

With them love became vocal and peripatetic. (Desire may be a better word, but at least it was a beginning.) It was a beginning when land-life had made, of necessity, fertilization internal and when the male had need to search for and find his mate. When the season is upon him the male will develop his new-found vocal chords and will croak or roar or bellow or sing, and some female will answer; and they will meet.

And then emotion will burst forth, rampant. Nor will it be only mere sensuality. It is excitement and the building up of excitement. The female, now producing within her body a fertilized and large and food-provided egg, has a much greater physiological task to face; all the more will she need to be 'triggered off' into a beginning, to be (to use anthropomorphic language, though do not give it too human implications) 'put into the right mood'. A lizard may lash his tail as might a fish; may suddenly open his highly coloured mouth, to startle, if not with beauty at least with flamboyance.

Birds of course are the great heirs to this elaboration of courtship, and very much the further elaborators of it. We must not look at that story for long, for we are not the descendants of the birds. But they and ourselves have common ancestors in the reptiles and all of life before, and there must be traces of like behaviour in us that will be all the more apparent now that we have sloughed off some of the grosser sexual habits of the mammals.*

Birds' life is governed by a series of emotional situations leading

* The bird has developed the floor of the brain, the *corpus striatum*, where we have developed the roof, the *cerebral cortex*. Sir Charles Sherrington in a beautiful book, *Man on His Nature*,[7] throws out the suggestion that an ideal creature would be one that combined in his head these two.

from one into the next. During the fallow winter—and here we are generalizing widely, writing of what we might call the type—the bird leads a neuter and asexual existence, probably in a flock: its major emotion will be the sort of communal sensitivity that enables the starling for instance to perform mass evolutions in flight as if the entity were the whole body of birds and not the individual— something of which our 'crowd mentality' may be the faint echo.

But it is when the spring comes that the birds awake to the sequence of their really intense emotions. The male feels the urge to migrate, at any rate to search out and mark out a territory for himself—if necessary at the expense of other and now rival males. The female follows. If the male is lucky some female will eventually respond to his urgent and passionate persuasion, his struttings, fluffings, attitudinizings, skilful aerial evolutions, the bright coat he has put on. There may be gift-bearing; later there will be another presentation, of nest-making material, not as we would take it as a 'gentle hint' but as a *release* of the mate's emotions that will start her off on the next step in the cycle of her progenitive actions. Then one day, being ready, she will succumb to the male's importunities, a true mating will take place. In pre-ordained and traditional ways she will lay and hatch her eggs and feed and tend her nestlings.

That is how bird life works out, a sort of inevitable pattern in time, a series of appropriate emotions brought forth by the behaviour of the other partner and themselves bringing forth the next necessary step in the business of love-making and mating and the producing and rearing of a family. The birds are utterly absorbed in the process—one could never credit a bird of paradise, extravagantly dressed and ridiculously hanging upside down though he may be to enhance the effect, with a feeling of self-consciousness. A lot of this is not entirely unreminiscent of the behaviour of human lovers.

However, these extremes of 'emotion by numbers', evolved by the birds from their cold-blooded but nevertheless noticeably passionate predecessors the reptiles, have never been practised by our own kind or 'class', the mammal. The need to produce a set pattern of external behaviour was not so pressing: a bird in one short season has to build her nest, hatch her eggs and feed with tremendous effort her ravenous and utterly helpless young; the mammal does much of the equivalent within her own body or at her breast, and her children are in varying degrees not so utterly dependent nor in such a terrible hurry to grow up.

Yet the mammals have of course the same need to procreate, and the same seasonal urge to do so. They are not lacking in rivalry and passion. Seals and walruses migrate for the purpose of breeding and then dispute between males for a patch of territory. Stags grow the equivalent of seasonal plumage in their fantastic antlers, and then dispute for the female (and as with the birds by no means always to the death, Nature being economical rather than romantic). Many small animals such as hares and squirrels court each other in delightful play.

It is play in particular perhaps that the mammal has developed. There is the play that is a preparation and training for the serious business of life. That is a matter of education and does not concern us here—except to observe that it must be a great developer of the imagination. But there is also sexual play, which often is parallelled by communal play. Birds too slip easily into this biologically useless but very pleasurable way of using up their surplus energy. The exercise of skill to impress the female, or in delightful company with the female, becomes a delight with a crowd. Swimming, diving, flying, sliding, galloping, running, playing hide-and-seek: the participant is completely lost, completely unselfconscious, and undoubtedly completely happy. One might bring in singing here as a kind of play. Birds' singing is not all rivalry; frogs surely don't croak in unison merely to make their presence felt; wolves must love baying in unison to the moon.

Mammals have one emotional outlet denied to the birds, which is that most intimate of operations, the giving of suck. There is I think a great deal of significance, as has already been suggested, in the bodily cosiness of the warm-blooded mammal—there is a phrase in Tolstoy's *Anna Karenina* describing her with her baby in her arms, which brings this successfully and justifiably up on to the human plane: 'that sweet scent of sleepiness and warmth that only children possess'. This is where true mother love as we understand it comes to life.

Mammals however, the large majority of them, still suffer from one disability that is also suffered by the birds and other vertebrates and indeed by nearly all sexed life that went before them. In a way it was a tyranny of sex though in another it was the reverse, a release. It might also be called an indignity. It is that the creatures concerned, both male and female, are only sexed in seasons. For a while interest in the other sex does not exist and both live side by side concerned only with the material job of earning a living. Then inexorably and inescapably sex returns, and with intensity. In mammals it is called the time of rutting, or, to use a scientific word, of *oestrus*—the scientific word being for once the apter, since its derivation is the Greek for a sting or goad, the maddening sting of passion. The higher Primates, ape and monkey (and also, it is said the tarsier though not the lemur), are released from this mechanical— or rather this chemical, for it is initially a change in the chemistry of the body—tyranny.

Now this is a blessing—a blessing it undoubtedly is, do not let us disbelieve that—from which much grief and difficulty is likely to flow. The female will now be not seasonally but permanently attractive to the male. There may be fluctuations in desire dependent on the female's menstrual cycle, but it is nothing like the shutting and opening of a tap which is oestrus and anoestrus. This will have a profound effect on the animal's social life. In insects the behaviour of the male and indeed his whole character is innate and pre-ordained, and that is that; in birds a married life certainly does exist, but it is for a season only and may not be renewed with the same pairing; in mammals subject to oestrus even so short a period of paired intimate life may not exist, either the male or female becoming re-absorbed into the neutral herd or the male disappearing to lead either a lone and bachelor or the equivalent of a men's-club existence. With the higher Primates however the position is different: the male, in common language, will stay around.

There exists in fact with man and ape and monkey the permanent incentive for family life. But there exists also the permanent incentive to promiscuity, to long, intense, passionate rivalries—in fact to all the emotional stresses and triangular or multilateral situations that in man give the basic material for the stories that he loves to tell himself, from Helen of Troy to the latest on the lending library's shelves. Nor is that way of putting it either cheap or misleading, for what interests man is what is important to man; and his personal relations, endowed as he is with such intensity of feeling, are indeed such. The formation of family life and social life was of

57

quite supreme importance to man and must have been so too to the stock from which he developed; and here, with the emancipation from the seasonal cycle of sex, we see the beginning of its formation, the possibility for it to be formed. And remember, there is very little inherited instinct to help in the formation. How easy to be an insect, how jolly to be a bird; but if you are an insect you may in a difficult situation bite off the tail end of the nursling to present it as food to the head end; if you are a bird you may fail to feed your young one at all because a fat and importunate cuckoo has kicked it out from the place where your instinct says it ought to be. The Primate way is the hard way. But it has, to say the least of it, possibilities.

What then of the other Primates, the apes and the monkeys, which we must allow at least to be our distant cousins? We need to be careful if we are to continue to draw conclusions from the ways of contemporary creatures, for it is after all the behaviour and emotional equipment of our ancestors that we seek to discover. There is however no other way; and if we keep in mind that we are dealing in probabilities not certainties we shall come to no harm. We shall not, that is to say, so long as at the same time we strive very hard to be objective. For the ways of the apes and monkeys are by no means wholly edifying. We must remember the accusations of the psychologists, that the behaviour we inveigh against most strongly is that which we really desire to indulge in ourselves. This doubtfully applies very far to the acts of monkeys and apes, but it may be a salutary thought.

Life, since ever it was sexed, has undoubtedly been over-sexed; it is Nature's insurance policy, her playing for safety—better too much than too little. The apes and the monkeys are certainly no exception to the rule. The keepers of monkey houses, while usually fond of their charges, have very low opinions of their morals or habits. But it would be unfair to judge by these creatures in their artificial boredom. It is only observations of Primates in natural and near-natural surroundings that will be worth considering. That has not been easy. To some extent it has been achieved with the anthropoid apes, but more particularly with the baboons, because they live usually in communities and in the open.

That baboons do live in communities—as do many other monkeys and often chimpanzees—is the first point to note about them. In spite of the disturbing and refractory elements of un-quiescent sex, a social life has been achieved.

Usually it seems a happy and contented community. To find enough food seems easy and there is much spare time. Mothers are nursing their young, perpetually examining their young. Everywhere one baboon is grooming another, grunting contentedly. The young are playing, are perhaps—for this is not all idyllic—bullying and being bullied. Sitting majestically alone, or suffering themselves to be groomed, are the 'overlords'.

'Male dominance'. Hamadryas baboon

So much will soon become apparent to the observer: that there are overlords, males who are dominant. The community is in fact a loosely knit one of close families, each of a dominant male and a 'harem' of possibly one but more usually two or three, up to six, wives with their children. Toting around with a family there may well be an 'unattached' bachelor or mature male.

Every individual in this community is keenly aware of his fellows. That is obvious from the alertness, the penetrating stares, sometimes threatening and placating gestures: perhaps things are not as serene as they seem. There may be a squeal of terror, which will alert everyone. Nothing more may happen—a child being bullied perhaps. But it may be the beginning of something much more serious. Some overlord, if the signs could have been read, has been slowly losing his predominance—his imperious stare is perhaps beginning to lose its power to quell. There now begins a terrible battle, which involves the whole colony. The bachelors in a moment have changed their roles and their natures, from as it were benign and contented uncles to lascivious, brave and ruthless contestants for one of the declining overlord's females. There will be lulls in the fight, inexplicable changes of sides, but it will not end until some bachelor has won that terror-stricken but passive female. She may well be dead, but she will have been won. The community licks its wounds, and settles down to a slightly changed balance of dominance.

So is the penalty of the unending goad of passion paid, at the expense of a death or two perhaps but never of the breaking up of the community. Yet to leave the picture painted in these terrible but romantic colours would be to give a wrong impression. Sex besides being relieved explosively is also relieved as one might say casually. There is a perpetual presenting of the hinder parts in a sexual invitation. It will not be restricted to an opposite sex or to the mature; it may or may not be taken advantage of. It will be used often in a kind of prostitution—to obtain a favour, to obtain protection, even to obtain access to an enemy, the inviter turning round to bite. It may even be used as no more, to quote Sir Solly Zuckerman, from whose book[8] much of this description is taken, than as a 'friendly greeting and a sign of good feeling'. . . .

So we see how a community of lower Primates is achieved by a system of 'polygyny maintained by dominance'. Since its essential feature is observed by most monkeys and apes it is at least likely that it was a system that the early hominids observed, that early man passed, if not through, at least out of. But more of that later. The only point we are making at this stage is that life so highly charged with feeling and emotion had been evolved from the vitality—the surplus energy and the surplus sex—of those higher forms of life which were man's progenitors.

It is not an easy situation from which to take over, not an easy nature that man inherited. However, do not let us leave this chapter obsessed by sex or obsessed by baboons. The essential of life is to perpetuate itself, and it is inevitable that the way of life should be primarily governed by the ways of progenitiveness. Only when there arrives a creature greater in aspects of mind and spirit than of body can that at all be altered.

Nor should we put the accent too heavily on monkeys and apes. The more significant truth is that man is a mammal and heir to all that is comprised in mammalhood. And that is a great deal, for the mammal is the culmination of an enormously long and successful evolutionary advance. We have traced that advance in terms of increase in feelings. It is a remarkable story. Now man is to come along and to take over—with, as tool, a bigger, better, more aware, more sensitive and more imaginative brain, in fact a new sort of brain altogether. He will have, as they say, a job.

5

The World Man Entered

THERE ought to be a picture, highly but not too portentously symbolical, depicting a supreme moment in time. It is of First Man, and behind him lie the trees and the forest and in front the open world. There is a light in his eye because he not only looks at that world but sees it; appreciates it; however dimly, considers it. The light in the eye, if only it could be depicted, would surely denote a compound of courage, excitement and fear. For from now on he will not merely suffer and adjust himself to the environment that faces him; he will come to grips with it and increasingly control it. From now on therefore it is going to be a different world; and the rate of change will be an acceleration.

Let us look at him a moment longer—ourselves not too starry-eyed. Besides a light in his eye he will undoubtedly have a flint in his hand. If there is a breeze he will not be sniffing it—he is not a snouted dog. Rather, with his keen eyes he will be looking in the direction from which it comes, and one day soon—one of God's days, that is, not ours—he will use the dog as the keeper of that sense of smell which he has lost for better things. He will be naked and as yet unashamed.

The picture indeed will not be altogether unlike the dismissal from the Garden of Eden. The other figures however will not be there. His wife, I think, will be otherwise engaged, too busy to stand and stare. And as for the avenging angel, the instrument of expulsion, he is invisible within the expanded box that through the millenia has been slowly created—the man's brain.

We need to know something ourselves of this world at which we imagine newly emerged man to be staring. For instance, the so familiar-sounding Ice Ages: how exactly do they come into the picture? What was the state of the world; what flora, what other fauna, did it contain?

Taking the god-like view where a thousand years is as it were only a single rhythmic breathing and a million years as it were a day, the answer to the last question is that man entered a unique world, singularly unlike anything that had been before. Geology teaches us this strange lesson, that the earth though solid is not unchanging; that the hills are not everlasting, nor the seas permanently confined, nor the heat of the sun entirely dependable. This planet has suffered, from its beginning, not only all sorts of comparatively minor fluctuations of climate but also from a major rhythm of vast upheavals or 'revolutions' that have occurred at intervals of something on average in the nature of 200 million years.

The world thus seen dozes for aeons in a climate warm and moist and equable and remarkably the same over most of its surface. Then it shakes itself into a fit of vast mountain-building that brings in its train a climate much keener and drier and of greater extremes of heat and cold. Slowly wind and water wear down the jagged mountains into milder slopes again, and finally equability—an equability disturbed no doubt by minor fluctuations—sets in once more.

Life has suffered from, has been challenged by, has taken advantage of these fluctuations; and so, as it were apart from and on top of these rhythmic changes, the face of the earth has slowly progressed to take on its present expression. The beginning and middle of the Paleozoic Era saw revolutions; the start of the Mesozoic saw one; so did the entry of the Cenozoic (*see* the table in Chapter I). The first of these seems to have set life really moving on its rapid evolutionary course, life in the waters that is to say. The second perhaps set life to invading the so far barren land. The third started the long innings of the giant reptiles that was also the great breeding and self-improving time of the insects and the plants. The fourth ushered in the age of the mammals and the birds.

And the fourth was about seventy million years ago; and man-the-mammal only begins to appear in the last single million of all those seventy.* This means that the age of the giant reptiles, and also the age of the 'coal measure' forests, where queer, scaly, palm-like, fern-like, flowerless and fruitless trees flourished, were both

* Such at least is the currently held belief; evidence to shift the date backwards needs to be more conclusive than at present before it is generally accepted.

already unimaginably remote when our semi-human ancestors came upon the scene. That is perhaps well known by now; but there used to be picturesque misapprehensions about it and we need to be reminded of the truth. It means too that man entered a world where bird and insect and tree and plant and flower were already pretty well as they are now—basically that is to say but without the influence of all man's own depredations and breeding and cultivation. There were probably more large ground-running birds about, and fair-sized reptiles; the grasses had only recently arrived; though in the tropics no doubt large and amazing flowers were attracting the insect, yet the herbaceous and the hedgerow flower was not so apparent, if only because the hedgerow and the gardener did not yet exist.

So far we have left out the mammals, and intentionally. There are three things to be said about them. First, they were still evolving when man arrived. Secondly, they had nevertheless somewhat quieted down in their evolutionary exuberance. Thirdly, they were prolific.

The first 'issue' of mammals, the fantastic, brainless gallumphers, had of course disappeared as surely as had the giant saurians. But there were some large and pretty strange beasts still abounding. The enormous tree-sloth may have still sat on his gargantuan haunches and browsed off trees; but man was not yet in America to watch him or to browse off his haunches. In Africa, which seems at that time to have been something of a museum of still-living anachronisms, such run-to-bone absurdities as Syndoceros, a deer with a kind of secondary pair of antlers above his muzzle, may still have existed, as did undoubtedly other strange beasts whose bones have been found with man-made flints and whom we shall meet in a later chapter. What really mattered to man however were not the freaks but the great run of animals with which we too are familiar, if only in zoos and often in a somewhat shrunken form: the elephant tribe and the hippo and rhino and more particularly the enormous army of the feeders on grass: deer, antelope, wild cattle, wild horse. *They* were there in their thousands upon thousands; as too no doubt were their enemies, all the cat tribe, and the wolves and the hyenas and the jackals. When men arrived the age of the mammals may have been on the wane, but it was certainly an ending with a kick in it and the world was more full of large wild beasts than we can see or imagine even after a visit to an African game reserve. What is more, they were clever and sensible beasts as well as large; evolution had discarded brainlessness long before the human animal arrived.

Mankind, then, entered a world that to all intents and purposes was our world—our world, that is to say, but fuller of beasts and empty of man. He did not enter, as he might well have done on the law of averages, a world lush, warm, watery, uncontrasted. He entered a world that was in every way the opposite.

That brings us to the great fact of the Ice Ages. We have left

The new and mighty tribe of grass-eaters

those to the end of this chapter so that we shall be more able to see them in perspective. Taking the long and wide view again, a 'Revolution' may or may not produce a series of Ice Ages. It at least brings about the possibility. The earlier revolutions may have done so; we do not know. The one ending the Paleozoic Era did produce one, freezing on that occasion the South more than the North. The last revolution also produced one, though belatedly—*and it was the one which mankind met.* This series, which is the only series with which we are concerned though not the only one that there has ever been, came when the Tertiary Era, the era of mammals, was just ended and what we have christened the Quaternary Era and the Pleistocene Period had begun. It came in the most recent million years of the Earth's history; and it lasted from roughly 600,000 to

10,000 B.C. It helped to end the evolutionary exuberance of the age of mammals—mankind is now finishing off the job—and it faced man himself with a challenge. It may even have been the making of man: not an unlucky chance that he did not arrive in geologically peaceable times but a lucky. It may even be that it was the very hardness of the times that evolved him.

One thing we must remember however. It is only, as we shall see, the later men, the Neanderthaler and *Homo sapiens*, who really faced the ice. These things are relative, and earliest man and half-man were only affected we might say secondarily. Over the long view, the gradual arrival of sharper, harder times had probably reduced the forests and driven him as an animal finally down from the trees. But when the Ice Ages first arrived their onslaught would merely drive him South again if he had ventured North and if he were already South give him a wetter climate for some thousands of years.

As is well known—and as is shown in the chart opposite—the coldness during the long half million years and more of the Ice Ages fluctuated tremendously. There were let-ups, times indeed when the higher latitudes were warmer than they are today—the second 'Interglacial' was an expanse of something like a hundred thousand years. But the ice came back. It came back, and at its worst the great glaciers reached the latitudes of London and even New York.

More of this in detail, as it affected man, in the next chapter. Here we are only concerned with the kind of world that man entered. There remains only to answer the natural question, why should there have been any Ice Ages at all?

We must not feel resentful about them. Indeed, balanced as we are on this globe at just the right distance from an unpredictable blazing sun, we should do well to regard any sort of climatic stationariness as a miracle and a blessing rather than anything at all otherwise as an unjustifiable imposition. The present belief is that the beginnings of an Ice Age will come not with a decrease in the sun's radiation but, surprisingly, with an increase. This will suck up more moisture; with the results of more rain, more snow, more cloud. Enough cloud, and in the higher latitudes the sun's summer warmth will be insufficient to melt the snow before the next winter comes. Then, if in particular there are high land masses towards the Pole

THE ICE AGES

GUESSES AT YEARS IN THOUSANDS	ICE black indicates advance of northern glaciers	MAN	PLUVIAL (SHADED) PERIOD (NEARER THE EQUATOR)
20	PRESENT INTERGLACIAL	Magdalanian Solutrean Aurignacian	
	FOURTH ICE AGE (WÜRM)	The Neander thaler	
100	THIRD INTERGLACIAL		
	THIRD ICE AGE (RISS)	The Various Hand-Axe Users	
200			
	SECOND OR GREAT INTERGLACIAL		
300		(Pithecanthropus included)	
	SECOND ICE AGE (MINDEL)		
400			
500	FIRST INTERGLACIAL	Australopithecus	
	FIRST ICE AGE (GÜNZ)		
600	Pre-glacial		

Chart to show, in a generalized way, the fluctuations of the Ice Ages
(Pluvial periods very approximate)

and these are cut off from the circulation of warm sea currents, the trouble and the hard-to-break sequence will have started: more snow means more cold—its very brightness reflects off the sun's heat—and more cold means yet more snow, which will pack down into ice, ever thickening, and which only a major change of climate or land formation or both will check.

Nevertheless, a check and a slow but certain reverse of the process does in the end take place. It took place for the last time—the last time to date—about 15,000 years ago. And if man owes much of a beneficial hardening process to the coming of the ice he probably owes the chance of achieving civilization (which chance he took) to its disappearance.

6

Homo faber

*H*OMO FABER: man the maker, the worker with tools. If you have lost the best and sharpest of your natural weapons, your fangs and your claws, you need a substitute. If, as the generations pass, your kind is meeting a continually harsher and colder world, if your lush tropical forest home is slowly changing for the worse, thinning, dying, then your need is all the greater. Primitive man had no illusions about the world owing him a living. He had to step out and seek it. He had to find a help for the job. He found it, paramountly, in the compressed remains of an earlier infinitesimal life of millions of years before him, the flint. Primitive man became—not quickly, but thoroughly and almost universally— the great, the admirable expert in making tools from stone. We name him, and rightly, with two Greek words: the old and ancient and original Stone Man, *Paleolithic*.

The first of the Paleolithic men were not *Homo sapiens*, indeed only the last of them had reached that status. This is I think a little surprising, and it needs to be thought about. With those 'evidences for ancestry' that we reviewed in the first chapter we proceed no further than Pithecanthropus before we find definite traces of stone tools, while by the time that we reach the low-browed but forceful Neanderthaler a second and cleverer method of knapping flint tools has been achieved.

Do not let us be too obsessed or worried by the difficult and arbitrarily given titles that abound in anthropology and archaeology, nor with the exact location or date or historical position of the bearers of them. For that matter there seldom is an exactness, and as time goes on new discoveries will no doubt alter the pattern. What we are going to follow in this chapter is the growth and spread of early man up to the time when *Homo sapiens* was about to appear,

and as made known to us by the belongings, the tools, in particular
the flints, that early man has left behind. It will be a factual chapter,
as factual as possible that is, leaving for the time being any speculation of what all this meant to the growing human mind. Fittingly
there is much solid material to go on, for if skeletons and skulls are
scarce, flint tools have been collected by the thousand so that our
museums are full of them: the silicous remains of the little sea
creatures are left when even our bones have decayed. Here too there
are a host of scientific names and a complicated interconnection;

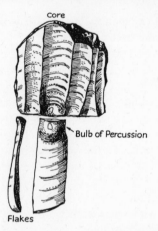

Core

Bulb of Percussion

Flakes

Flint-making. Take your core and knock flakes off
it; you can then concentrate on either core or flake

but once more it does not matter greatly if they and their sequence
are not mastered. What matters is the skill and mind of man: the
broad picture of his surprising emergence.

The first thing to be noticed about a flint is that if it is broken it
produces a remarkably sharp edge. That is easy—once, that is to
say, you possess a mind that notices and remembers and connects.
These no doubt were the first two stages: either to find a broken
flint and to use it, or to break one intentionally. The result of the
second act has been called an *eolith*, the 'dawn-flint', and great con-
troversy has raged as to which of such questionable finds were
natural and which were genuinely man-made. But that was more in
the time when the very antiquity of man itself had to be established,

70

and the dispute has now lost its importance. It is of course tantalizing not to know whether African Australopithecus, upright but less than half-brained, used or made 'eoliths'. But there must have been such an early stage, and if so it is a fair assumption that this creature, near whose bones were found the skulls of baboons broken by what look like well-aimed blows, had progressed so far. Pithecanthropus had reached a stage further.

That stage is to take a flint and *make a tool out of it*. Hit a slab of flint a sharp blow and there is knocked out a solid cone in something the shape of a limpet shell. There is your raw material to work upon. Take it, take a smaller stone as a hammer, or preferably a

A well-made 'hand-axe'

piece of bone or hard wood, and tap obliquely near the edge. If you have the knack a long thin flake will slide off. You can either use the flake as a tool or go on with your 'knapping', ever more delicately, until your core has become an edged tool.

Sinanthropus, Pekin Man, did both these things, in rather a primitive and haphazard way, though as we have said his material was a difficult one, quartz. After this there begins to arrive the 'hand-axe' proper, normally a core and not a flake implement, shaped typically like a great flattened pear, with a tip and a double edge extending to near the rounded base.

Now here is a *standard implement*, not haphazard, but regularized, produced by the same basic method again and again, a method that has been learned. This tool spread, with variations, over pretty well the whole of the then inhabited globe, from the Cape to the site of

71

London, from Algiers to India. It lasted, basically, for something in the nature of ten thousand generations of near-men.*

That is a staggering thought. We can well expect progress to be slow, understand that it will be a help for tradition not to suffer rapid change. But ten thousand generations ! It is a biological figure not an historical, a figure of physical evolution rather than cultural. It shows, I think, how much of animal there still remains in the make-up of these ancient and primitive 'users of hands', these men of, as the archaeologist names them, the Lower Paleolithic ('Lower' because his flints are found, being older, in a lower strata of the ground). It shows too, one would think, that man, or primitive man at least, is not unlike the rest of animal life in that it seems to need the goad of change in environment to prick him into rapid evolutionary advance. The larger part of the reign of the hand-axe takes place in the long stretch of the second inter-glacial period when the lion and his like could live in the latitude of Southern England and when the favoured homes of men, Africa and Southern Asia, must have been a paradise of equable stability approaching almost to the near-everlasting summers that the world seems to have lost.

There was change of course. Yet the pattern remained: a little different, a little better, slightly adapted, but of course and without question the same basic design. There must have been intense pride in the making of these flints—that in itself may have been a factor resisting change. Often the same phenomenon has been reported, both by archaeologists and also by anthropologists observing such remaining flint-users of today as the Australian aborigines: only the best will do; tool after tool is thrown away, unused or with no trace of use, until the craftsman has reached his own high standard. There is a hand-axe discovered near Maidenhead so large and beautifully made that—such is the imaginative suggestion—it might well have acted as a sort of heirloom, a tribal treasure, the forerunner of the weapon hanging on the baronial wall, the hand-axe of all hand-axes. The kind of knapping that a good hand-axe needs is not easily done; it is no mere hitting of one stone with another, but the careful taking of the core in the hand and the sliding away of thin slice after slice with pressure of body behind a bone or wooden tool and the easing of skilful fingers. Its execution was surely the first skilled trade.

* i.e. for something over 300,000 years, with three or four generations to the century.

72

Now what were the uses of this universal tool? The simplest and easiest answer is that that is indeed what it was, a universal tool. There is no question of proper hafting yet—if efforts were made to bind it into a cleft stick the chances are, I should imagine, that it fell out pretty often. The hand-axe—*coup de poing*, fist weapon, the French discoverers called it—is a heavy thing, but its rounded base does fit well into a human hand—a big and strong hand.

Some say the hand-axe was used essentially for digging up roots. Others declare that a strong stick of hard wood is better for that job. Yet others, who have tried, say that it is very good for puncturing the skin of a dead beast and then for flaying it. We must be careful here, for however slow is change a people at one end of a hundred thousand years or of the face of the earth will not be the same as at the other end. Early or 'Lower' Paleolithic Man is often described as a 'food gatherer', and that is a vague and possibly misleading term. You don't 'gather' a boar or a bison, at least not until he is dead. Arboreal creatures are likely to be omnivorous: insects, grubs, young shoots, fruit, nuts. They are not herbivorous; you need a very special digestion before you can successfully live on grass, Nebuchadnezzar notwithstanding. The same applies presumably to the half-men who had come down from the trees. The picture of them merely picking the sub-tropical equivalent of blackberries and 'grubbing' for roots is not a very complimentary and a slightly ridiculous one. Even a near-half-sized cerebral cortex is a formidable instrument; and man had his hands and his eyes—not to mention his hunger. He must at a fairly early stage have become a meat-seeker—a hunter, or perhaps more accurately a trapper. A hanger-on he may have been at first to the edge of the herd, and, summoning up his courage, a destroyer of the weak and sick. He may have been even a scarer of the vulture and a diner off the dead: primitive man has no objection to high meat, as Charles Darwin observed of the Tierra del Fuegians whom he observed returning triumphantly from an expedition with huge collars of reeking flesh around their necks. From this, man graduated no doubt to the laying of traps and the killing of the so disabled animals—itself a sufficiently dangerous job. Until however there are flint-pointed spears the real 'hunt' as we visualize the term can hardly have come into existence.

.   .   .   .   .

73

Now all that by no means belittles early Paleolithic Man, nor questions his courage. He was, as has been said, a small and lonely creature amongst a world of still teeming, self-confident and very imposing beasts. It will be well to try to visualize him and his fellow travellers of the animal kingdom in the wide empty world of say two to four hundred millenia away. His home is typically, probably initially, South and East Africa or South East Asia. We shall be well advised incidentally to stop asking where is the 'cradle of the human race'. Unless chemical or atomic dating methods improve very considerably and until we find many more fossils there is no way of telling with anything approaching certainty where the human race started, and in any case it may just possibly have started in more places than one. Nevertheless a really warm climate where there had been much forest does seem a necessity; and the two areas mentioned do fill the bill as well as giving good trace of occupation. Of the two, Africa gives us as yet less fossil remains but much greater finds of flints.

We can I think quite fairly help ourselves here with a large generalization. Ignoring all the minor variations both in tools and users, we will make four great divisions and so give a potted history of nearly half a million years like this:

First: Australopithecus type.   No known tools.
Second: Pithecanthropus type.   The hand-axe.
Third: Neanderthal type.   Flake tools.
Fourth: *Homo sapiens*.   Flake and bone tools in variety.

That is to jump the gun a little in the narrative, but it should prove useful. First Australopithecus, the upright but small-brained creature found with bashed-in baboon skulls in Bechuanaland.

Him we have already dismissed as not probably a tool maker. But if he was roving the open countryside upright and with hands free he *must* have found use for those hands: he picked up and used sticks and stones, that is a reasonable assumption. If he opened the skulls of baboons—to obtain and eat the brains in all probability—then he showed more directed skill than any animal shows; if, armed with his basher, he killed the baboon in fair fight, then he has gone a great deal further and has started the ascendancy of man over the rest of creation. That is about all we can safely say. We shall do better to go on to Pithecanthropus, who used a primitive hand-axe.

The Pithecanthropus sort of person then; a little more advanced perhaps than Pekin Man (who had only rough quartz tools you will remember) and so living a few thousand generations later, say 400,000 years ago or 300,000—incredibly it does not make so very much difference which. He will be roaming the open countryside of Kenya or Tanganyika or Nyasaland, with his flint in his hand and, very urgently, seeking what he may devour. Like all life, he is tied to water, though the cord is loose; he will not stray very far from the lake-side, the river, the water-hole—neither will the beasts for whose flesh he has already acquired a hesitant and perhaps guilty

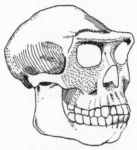

Reconstructed skull of
Pithecanthropus

taste. He will be naked. Will he be hairy?—nobody knows, and though hair is a birthright of the mammals they do not always accept it or appear to need it, man included; nevertheless, one imagines, hairier than ourselves. He will be not much over five foot in height; he will stand and walk very much, though perhaps not quite, as a man.

Viewed from behind our Pithecanthropine marauder would be seen to have a thick and tremendously powerful neck and a head that seems the wrong shape, much too broad and not half high enough. If he turned we should undoubtedly be shocked: flat nose, no chin, jaw prognathous and jutting beyond the flat nose, receding forehead and, perhaps most striking of all, a prominent ridge along the line of the eyebrows, a projecting pent-house shelf that rides right across the face above the eyes and nose. If he bared his teeth they will be seen as large but not inhuman.

Somehow with his weapons and his skill the Pithecanthropines around Pekin killed great quantities of deer. His kind in East Africa had a much more formidable collection of animals to contend with. Africa as it were lagged behind; more than halfway through the Pleistocene Period it still supported creatures that elsewhere in the world had become extinct. There is a by now famous site of early man discovered and excavated by Professor Leakey and his wife, lying forty miles South-West from Nairobi and called Olorgesailie. Through the long ages of hand-axe using there lay here a lake, rising and falling, spreading and receding, as rainy centuries or millenia followed drier ones. Here, at the various shore-levels left to the anthropologist to study and number and systematize, these ancient predecessors of ours have left their weapons together with the bones of the creatures they ate. Here, from *The Prehistory of East Africa*[4] by Sonia Cole, is a description of these beasts:

'At horizon 7, the main diet seems to have been the giant baboon, *Simopithecus* (who must have tasted very nasty); at level 8 it was the large and probably very tough horse, *Equus olduvaiensis*, while at level 10, Acheulian* man mainly hunted the giant pig *Notochoerus*, which was almost as big as a modern rhino. In sands between occupation levels 5 and 6, many fossil remains were found, including the hippopotamus with periscopic eyes, *Hippopotamus gorgops*.'

The horse mentioned here is a 'true' horse, but a three-toed horse was also contemporaneous with the hand-axe users, together with an extinct and outsize representative of the ox, sheep, elephant and giraffe respectively, the last-named, a heavy, huge-horned creature, being a beast that early man in Africa did manage to skin and eat even if he did not always or ever kill it himself.

One other discovery is of interest from this breeding ground of man and beasts in East Africa, and that is a number of fairly well-shaped stone balls. It is suggested that they may have been used for grinding and pounding roots, and no doubt for the children, if they got the chance, to play with. But, more intriguing, some of the balls were found in groups of three. This suggests the *bolas*, an instrument

* i.e. user of the Acheulian flints, the main 'culture' of hand-axes and named (as are so many) after the French site where they were first found.

of three balls tied together with thongs that is thrown to entangle the feet of wild horses and cattle. The caballeros of South America used them in the last century, Charles Darwin[9] on his visit to those parts even having a try at their use but only succeeding in tripping up his own horse: if that guess is a good one then these earliest men were cleverer in at least one respect than the great man who startled the world by first regarding them as his ancestors. But the question arises (since the balls were not pierced) how were they tied together? On the other hand, why else in groups of three?

We have recorded—and the evidence is incontrovertible—that the hand-axe user existed not only in Africa but widely over Europe and Asia. That means an existence often in much colder climates; and though there may have been more than one origin of man yet as many as there were are likely to have been staged in kindly and favourable places. We must believe then that man, like any other species once it has begun to seize the evolutionary chance, 'deployed' rapidly and extensively.

Rapid it was in terms of biological time, but historically he had many, many centuries to do it in. Nevertheless the extent of it is impressive, and, to us who read throughout history of 'nomads' but who can hardly visualize the life, even somewhat astonishing. The truth is of course that man as yet could be nothing but a nomad. Pekin Man's remains were found in a cave, but that so early in the story is exceptional. The hand-axe and the growing skill of the hands behind it were no doubt stripping boughs to make a wind-break for the night. But even so the idea of 'home' could hardly yet exist. Man was a roamer. So too were often the beasts on which he depended increasingly for a livelihood. And sometimes too, no doubt, if man roamed far enough he came across new beasts. . . .

Man's ability to wander extensively was enormously helped by an indirect result of the Ice Ages. So much water was locked up in vast thicknesses of ice in wide circles round the poles that the level of the sea was lowered: all through the Pleistocene Period Britain for instance was widely joined to the continent (the break came about 5000 B.C.), and at its maximum the height of the land above the sea during these times was as much as 400 feet greater than it is at present. Now 400 feet vertical makes a deal of difference: there was much more land. The Mediterranean during the glaciations was no more than two great lakes, one each side of a land arm through Sicily; the

Red Sea must have been much more easily crossed; there was no need to swim the Hellespont; and the East Indies were more of an isthmus than an archipelago. In other words Africa-Europe-Asia was virtually one great land mass, with mankind free to go where he willed—always assuming of course that he had the determination to cross or bypass the mountains, the lakes and the rivers (but not much in the way of deserts), and in particular to face or suffer the climatic changes involved. To complete the story, he could no doubt at any of the times of maximum glaciation have crossed by an Aleutian land bridge into the Americas, but it would certainly have needed some hardihood to do it and only it is believed at the end of the last Ice Age was the feat accomplished; Australia, once also joined to S.E. Asia but separated long before man's arrival, he probably colonized, by island-hopping and with the aid of raft or canoe, during that same Ice Age, say 50,000 years ago.

By the most patient search for evidence from the moraines and

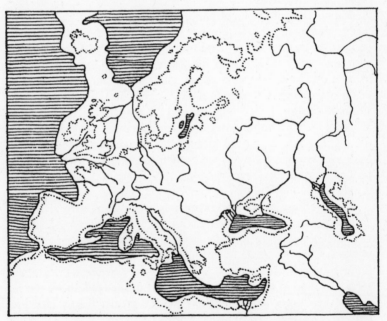

Man was a rover—with land bridges to help him rove. Probable *maximum* elevation during the Ice Ages of the coastline of North Africa and Western Europe—this would not happen anywhere at one time

ice-deposits in the Alps there has been gained a remarkable knowledge of the great Ice Ages. The outstanding discovery is that they were in the plural, not one long freeze but a series of fluctuations producing four glaciations (which even in themselves had as it were pulsations) and three warm intervals in between. The diagram in the previous chapter gives a better idea of these than words can, always remembering that dates are very approximate.

As the cold climate swayed North and South the kind of creatures that had evolved to fit it swayed too. And man? To say that man followed would be too much of an over-simplification—just how he moved and how much he moved can never be known in detail. But at least we can say this: the world-wide changes in climate and land formation that went with the successive glaciations must have been the major factor in the movements of early man.

And not only does this apply to his movements but to his whole way of life and development as well. The people who spend their life seeking, or avoiding, musk ox, bison, reindeer, mammoth, cave lion, cave bear, will be leading a very different existence from those, whom we have already described, whose neighbours were wallowing hippo and giant pig and baboon—for one thing they are likely to need different tools. The person who knows frost and ice and what the North wind is like is going to meet problems and hardships never dreamt of by Pithecanthropus in the semi-tropics. Either he will be a different person from the start or he will become one.

Now when did man first appear in Europe and the Northern latitudes of Asia? The difficulty in answering that question is that though it is often easy to tell, from the animal bones found with his own, whether a man had lived in either a glacial period or an interglacial, it is not so easy to tell which period it is in the series. However, things are gradually getting themselves sorted out and a fairly certain picture can be given.

So far as Asia is concerned the answer is simple: no sign as yet of anything in the North until a much later date. The Northern half of Asia is not likely to have been hospitable, at least since the Himalayas arose in late Miocene times and the world began to become sharply zoned and cold. But it is also true that the huge area has not yet been searched with anything like the thoroughness of for instance Britain or France. In Ice Age Europe on the other

79

hand it is obvious that the hand-axe men must have existed, since their tools, called Abbevillian, Chellean, Acheulian, have been named after finds made in France. The naming is an historical accident: the fact that, a hundred years before the dried lake bed at Olorgesailie was found strewn with them, an enthusiastic and determined Frenchman by the name of Jacques Boucher de Perthes was in his spare time collecting hand-axes and struggling to convince the scientific world that they were the work of man. We do not have to go all the way back through the four Ice Ages however. Pithecanthropine man, born probably as a species while the barren North was beginning its second Ice Age, flourished through the long spell of the second inter-glacial. It would probably mean not so much warmer as drier weather where he lived. And he would have had no difficulty in wandering into Europe—which he probably did. Either that is the truth, or else his 'culture', that is to say his *expertise* in making tools, penetrated the North and men that were very much like him ('Heidelberg' men) adopted that culture.

Then these first Europeans of the second long inter-glacial, whoever they were, seemed to show more discretion than valour— one can hardly blame them—and to retreat Southward as the cold returned. The first evidence of a whole race of people successfully withstanding the rigours of living on the edge of the icelands so that it might hunt and live on their fauna comes only with the fourth and last glaciation. That race was the Neanderthalers.

We must go carefully here, in view of what was said in Chapter I. The Neanderthal Man who came to Europe and who stayed there until he met *Homo sapiens* is, or became, what has been called the 'extreme' Neanderthaler; the 'generalized' type either stayed in or spread into the kinder climates of the Mediterranean and Africa and Southern Asia. It is the extremist that we are interested in, the type that used to be called simply Neanderthal Man. It was he who first had the courage and hardihood to face the bitter weather and not turn tail—and if in the process he was turned into even more of a lumbering lout and finally specialized himself out of existence we should at the very least pay him passing respect. History rests with him rather than his less adventurous Southern cousins.

Before we go North however: what happened to Pithecanthropus, flint-using half-brained man?

Possibly he fell before the new arrivals, the Southern generalized

Neanderthaler, either by slaughter or new disease, or from pure discouragement. But the finding of isolated fossils must not drive us into thinking in terms of immutable types. That is just what Nature is not, immutable; and man was then still sufficiently an animal one would imagine for ordinary physical evolution to have its play. The genes of more suitable teeth, better walking limbs and —this overshadows all else—bigger and better brain, were no doubt flourishing and perpetuating; and vice versa. Pithecanthropus may simply have slowly faded and the 'generalized' Neanderthaler

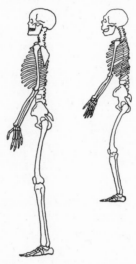

Contrasted skeletons and stances of
modern man and the Neanderthaler

slowly dawned. Most probably his disappearance was due to a combination of the two causes, with as they say local variations—and what that could mean in human dramas of anguish and jealousy on the part of the biologically 'unselected' on the one hand or of man-hunting and murder and sudden death on the other, must be left to the imaginations of those who wish to exercise them.

The Northern Neanderthaler then, let us finish this chapter by considering him: the tragic fellow who stayed to face the ice and suffered as a reward. We have reached now, it must be realized, the last glaciation: the past is at length not hundreds but only some tens of thousands of years ago.

First his appearance. Were we to meet him our first impression would be I think that here was a massive man—not tall but strong and solid. The second would almost certainly be that here was a very ugly creature and not much of an improvement on Pithecanthropus. The head is bigger, the brain is bigger obviously; but for the rest there is the same eyebrow ridge, the same chinless muzzle-like mouth and jaw, receding forehead. As for stance and gait, it is if anything less upright, more shambling than his predecessor's.

Next his tools. These are called by the archaeologist 'Mousterian', which is confusing, particularly when the Neanderthaler is, as sometimes happens, called Mousterian himself. It arises from his flints having been discovered before many of his skeletons and before the connection between the two was apparent: two great amateurs,

Neanderthaler's flints—to cut
and scrape and flay

French and English respectively, Edouard Lartet and Henry Christy, first found these tools in caves near the village of Le Moustier in the Vézère valley of Southern France. The essential change from the long hand-axe culture is that now a *flake* tool is usually made, what is struck off the flint core and not the core itself. The process entails the careful choosing of the right shaped core and the more careful planning of just how and where to strike. The results are lighter and more handy tools than the great hand-axe—an embryo knife, a scraper, an awl for piercing holes.

What was the Neanderthaler piercing and scraping? That answer can be given fairly certainly: the skins of animals, to be used as covering. For even the miserable and degenerate Fuegians wore skins when they could come by them, and their climate can have been little better nor their hardihood less than the Neanderthaler's. In fact we see now for the first time a man clothed—and a man, too, living in a house, at least a winter home, a limestone cave, as he did at Le Moustier, as he did in 'Kent's Cavern' in an un-lush and tundra-covered Devonshire. Almost it seems, by comparison with the slow-changing animalishness of the past, we reach modernity.

And yet of course how far we are away! He had fire, this man, and no doubt carried the precious live thing about with him, duly muzzled and damped down. He cooked his meat with his fire. He buried his dead. He surely must have clothed himself. He faced the hyena, in dispute perhaps for the deer that the sabre-toothed tiger had slain and sucked and abandoned; he faced and perhaps trapped and killed the mammoth and the bison. But his set of tools is really meagre in the extreme and he shows little inventiveness. His spear

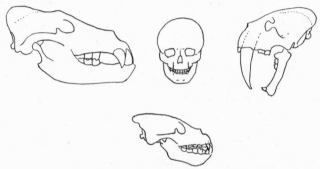

Man's rivals: cave bear, hyena and sabre-toothed tiger. Bigger teeth; smaller brains

was only a wooden one and he makes very little use, as his successor does, of ivory or bone. There is too a sense of squalor in his dis-covered caves—'the hearth and the bones from innumerable meal-times,' says Mr. Bibby in *The Testimony of the Spade*,[10] 'lie scattered over the floors . . . his home must have looked—and smelled—like the lair of a wild beast.'

Neanderthaler in the North in fact did not thrive. He hung on, and for a long time. He paved the way. He was brave, undoubtedly; but he was not very clever. His heart, but not his brain, was in the right place: that might be his epitaph.

Before we follow the fate of *Homo neanderthalensis* and the rise of *Homo sapiens* we must devote a chapter to considering what can be done, in fact what has to be done, with a brain that is both big and rightly shaped.

7

Man Had to Think

M AN is outstandingly a conceptual thinker. That short statement, which certainly needs elaboration, covers as nothing else can the essential difference between ourselves and the rest of creation. If 'the best out of a hundred' were given for a person's powers of conceptual thinking, Einstein we would allow perhaps 99 and ourselves as we say nowhere. But bring in the apes and the monkeys, the dogs and the horses, the 'cunning' fox and the 'wise' owl, and the picture would be very different: say Einstein, 99; you and I, 90; the animals, 5 downwards. Not more than five; though more, you will note, than nothing at all.

The practical Horatio, you will remember, is startled by Hamlet's exclamation: 'My father—methinks I see my father.'

'Where, my lord?'

'In my mind's eye, Horatio.'

In the mind's eye: *that* is where men see so much. And the animals? Very little it would seem that is not impinging upon their brain from the physical eye of here-and-now.

A definition of concept is needed. Latin, *concipere*, to take together. A concept then is an idea, again 'in the mind's eye', of a thing or many things which we consciously and at will draw up from the present scene or from the storehouse of our memory, in order to think about it. It is something not only wholly immaterial but, if necessary, wholly divorced from the immediate present. *We* have brought up this thing to think about; it has not been primarily presented to us. We take up this idea of a thing, and consider it, and mentally look around it. Just as we can take a physical thing in our clever hands and examine it with our keen eyes, so we take the immaterial idea of a thing and hold it up and balance it in our minds

84

and examine that. We compare, the present with the past, the possible future with the present; we draw conclusions.

Disappointingly, sadly, animals can do very little of all that; despite all the 'cleverness' of our pets, we really, if we consider dispassionately, know that this is likely to be so. Our dog is a miracle of loving and sensitive response; but shut him the wrong side of a gate and he will go on scratching, wellnigh interminably with the same motion, and make no effort to find a way round. It is a matter, essentially, of possessing either an undeveloped or a developed frontal area of the brain—the frontal or 'silent' area being that place you will remember where the connections are not at all with the prime senders of messages from the outside world but only, as a managing director will only see reports from his staff, with the brain centres that receive those messages. Here are the *association centres*, the part of the brain that, as we said, cogitates and considers; remembers and compares; associates; worries out.

If Australopithecus had the beginnings of such powers, if Pithecanthropus had more of them, the Neanderthaler yet more and *Homo sapiens* much more, how did these species of half-men and men manage to acquire them? That is what we need to consider, together with what it was like, so far as we can imagine it, to be all and any of these people who were in process of acquiring this excellent frontal brain.

It must have been essentially a process of use and disuse. That is a suspect phrase amongst evolutionists, though Darwin used it; there need be no suggestion however of ruling out natural selection— the lemuroid who failed to use his eyes got pounced upon, the paleolithic bride preferred perhaps the man who used his brain to the man who only used his biceps. Success then, we may believe, went to the potent user of that most potent trio, hand, brain and eye, and who also refrained from using, or responding to, that automatic, emotional urge from the lower parts of the brain that sets the dog scratching everlastingly at the gate—a matter of control by inhibition.

Once more we will go back, very briefly, to the apes and the mammalian stock, to see what sort of mental equipment, good or bad, man may have been presented with. We say an elephant never forgets, largely on the evidence of one vindictive specimen who hosed his ex-tormentor after a period of twenty years. That does not show intelligence so much as the power to revive a deep emotional experience: there is a scar on the brain, and any element of the original experience will inevitably exacerbate it. This is not to deny that memory is a miraculous phenomenon, or emotion a powerful one; but it all has little to do with conceptual thinking. That same elephant or his like, or for that matter his more distant relatives in the families of dog and bear and lion and horse and monkey, may be able to do all sort of tricks, in or out of the circus. He—they—have acquired the skill, the know-how, the habit; in physiological language the fore-brain, having learnt the process, has pushed it back and down into the more automatic brain. That again is marvellous; but it is the property of most brains however small and is indeed little more than an essential economy measure, leaving the higher parts free for further learning. What matters is, how quick was the learning.

We could spend hours learning about animals' learning, because so much work has been done on it, so many experiments made. We will not do so. For one thing the evidence is often inconclusive and the findings of the experimenters not above the suspicion of bias, though no doubt unconscious bias. For another the findings are sometimes what any fool could have told the experimenter before he started. The experiments hinge round the idea of setting the animal a simple problem, with some incentive to his solving it—usually the reward of food. He has to get out of a cage for instance by undoing a latch; he learns that much and then the mechanism is changed. One central fact comes out of all this: that there are two sorts of learning, either by trial and error and then the slow memorizing of it so that it is relegated to a habit; or by what is called 'insight', that is to say by observing the facts presented—all of them, upwards from the simple one of 'oh, the latch has been turned the other way round!'—and by drawing the correct inferences from them and acting accordingly.

Not always, when due allowances are made for the animal's physical make-up and way of life, is it the Primate who wins in these competitions, nor does every anthropoid ape by any means beat at the game every monkey. Indeed one of the more unexpected results has been the discovery of the variety of character in all mammals— to be a genius is not solely a human attribute. Nevertheless it is the ape that, as a kind, shows the greatest powers of insight. So much so that the cleverest ape, the chimpanzee, has been set much harder tasks and has succeeded. There is the famous ape of Wolfgang Köhler's who, seeing a banana suspended out of reach, and also a packing case lying handy, put the case under the banana, climbed on the case and reached the banana.

Indeed there was the cleverer ape who piled up two packing cases and also took a stick to knock down the suspended food.

Now this is certainly 'insight', this is 'observing all the facts presented and drawing the correct conclusions'. It is really more, it is choosing from the facts presented. It is using the memory, the

Skill of hand, brain and eye:
making a flint

memory of what can be done with a stick and with boxes; it is the taking of facts and memories and putting them together—*concipere* —it is conceptual thinking.

It is also the ultimate triumph of the apes—and it was a pretty ramshackle affair at that, with the boxes about to fall down any minute. It was from there, or thereabouts, we may imagine, that Australopithecus took over. He had indeed a long and uphill road to tread.

Of course that last is itself an assumption: modern apes may have deteriorated in intelligence from the creature, whatever exactly it may have been, that was their and our ancestor. Nevertheless it is a reasonable accumption that somewhere along the line was a being of about equal intelligence to the chimpanzee. It is also fairly obvious, hardly disputable, that it is the acquiring of the power of conceptual thinking that brings creation over the threshold out of the darkness of the animal kingdom into the light—a confused and confusing light—of manhood. For man is by our definition the tool maker; and *that* power certainly needs the prior power of conceptual thinking, of thinking for instance: 'a sharp edge cuts; a broken flint has a sharp edge; I will break a flint!'

Baboons are said to hurl down rocks on to their enemies, though this is only doubtfully true. Monkeys and apes will throw things with purpose; a chimpanzee will use a stick as a sort of spoon, picking up ants on it and licking them off; a few very clever chimpanzees have as we have seen genuinely used a stick as a tool.* But no animal so far as is known has ever consciously *made* a tool. That is why, I think, it was right to call the first man Paleolithic Man, to put the accent from the start on to his ability, his varied and slowly expanding ability, to make tools out of flint. For the flint tool was itself the maker of so many more tools, from the simple pointed stick for root-grubbing to, later, the arrow shaft and the bone needle. It was also surely a tool calling forth great skill in use as well as to make, a real tool compared with the child's-play of fooling and beating around with a wooden stick. And it is a point very much worth making that once you have really begun to use tools you are using your hands that direct the tool, and your brain that directs the hands, in an altogether new way greatly superior to anything managed by the animal whose body and limbs—teeth, jaw, pincers, claws and paws—are themselves the tools.

Hand, brain and eye are in fact still at work as the powerful trio, the great trinity; but one partner, brain, has taken the lead and indisputably assumed the senior partnership. Its owner, driven by ambition or necessity, or by the Life Force, or by God who had chosen him from out of all the animals for the great role, was going to tax it heavily; and, pretty well, it was going to stand up to the strain. Let us try to see a little in what ways the tool-using predecessor of *Homo sapiens*, from Pithecanthropus to Neanderthal Man, was increasing at one and the same time his skill and his power to think.

---

* Not *kept* one. Recent reports on 'Paris', a chimpanzee in the Moscow Zoo, bear this out. Paris cleans his nails with a piece of thin wire—when he finds a piece of thin wire.

The first thing to realize is that man—we can by now give that simple title—was a highly educable creature. With the mammal's slow increase of brain had come a slow increase in the length of childhood, that is to say of dependence. To be a child for long is to give hostages to fortune as surely as to have a child. No other species has as it were dared to let its young remain dependent for so many years. It was however an apparently risky investment that turned out both gilt-edged and bearing a high rate of dividend. We may imagine the baby Pithecanthropine learning to use his hands and brain by endless play, by watching and imitating its mother, later being initiated into the hereditary skill of the knapper, earlier (and no doubt in the positive and proverbial way) being initiated into the terrible might of fire. Perhaps fire stimulated his imagination, as well it might above anything else in his early experience: someone has called it 'the terrible red flower' and so it must have seemed to man. Animals it terrified. Only man dared to stand up to it, then to use it and control it, and finally to make it and renew it. And whoever was the true Prometheus who had this temerity, he does seem to have been a very early man. Yet, early though he was, the awe remained: it was the live thing; it was perhaps symbolic of life; it should, both for practical and magical reasons, never be allowed to die. When you trekked you took it with you, duly tamed and smothered, on your journey. . . .

Even trekking itself must have been a liberal education. Gorillas wander within the confines of their forest in search of the young shoots that are their favourite food, and at the end of the day make themselves a sort of nest in which to sleep: the same food always, the same sketchy lair. But man when he wandered in search of new food, or followed the beasts that had become his food, would certainly not meet the same situations. The material for yesterday's wind-break would not necessarily be available today; and building it would not be a matter of habit but of ingenuity—not merely the clever ape picking up a stick for a purpose because he sees it handy, but visualizing the stick or the branch and searching for it, and if not finding it making do with something else. Food too: what rash and brave experiments, what hesitations and what tragedies, must have occurred as man learnt to distinguish between the edible and the poisonous. What admonitions there must have been for that matter, what warnings and traditions handed down; what old wives' tales even, on the subject of good to eat and bad to eat and bad to eat at certain times. Then, however simple your life and virtually non-existent your belongings, you would need to *carry* things. Perhaps a string about the middle, the first belt, would be invented: into that the sticks and weapons could be tucked. But food, and in particular water, would need to be carried. We who can get made a tin can for less expense than it takes to pick and prepare the fruit or the drink within it can hardly imagine how hard put to it Early Stone Age Man must have been to hit upon even the most elementary of containers. Australian aborigines, who like early man have no pottery, use shallow bowls of wood or bark, or a bag of animal hide, or even a human skull—and that will leak along the sutures if it is not stuck up with gum. Before needle and thread, gum is perhaps another unexpected precious need; and the finding and using of it another stimulator of the brain.

There must however have been many more personal, emotional things of which man was made aware, and, once conceptual thinking was achieved, made so much more vividly aware. One would be his own body: if you walk horizontally and have a snout and no hands you will know surprisingly little of your body, except something of its feel and smell. Another awareness will be of other people's bodies. The higher Primates, apes and monkeys, have both those awarenesses; and their resultant behaviour is not edifying (though not so ugly if one manages to avoid regarding it anthropomorphically). If on the other hand you are a creature who has gained the ability to think of the *idea* of another person, to remember and consider that other body when it is not there, then 'person' becomes real and 'body' more than something merely warm and pleasant to react to in automatic and entirely unthinking ways. I think too that the expressiveness of the human face must have helped a great deal in dragging man up from the lower brutishness of personal and sexual relationships. As an instance, someone has pointed out that it is only in man that the whites of the eyes are really seen, which adds immensely to their expressiveness, to the significance of their movements. It is not that monkeys and apes are unaware of each other as individuals; with their jealousies and systems of dominance they are highly aware. But it is an awareness of the moment only, and proximity seems to swamp almost everything but the most sensual (not necessarily but usually sexual) reactions. Köhler tells of his chimpanzees' most touching solicitude towards one of their number who was sick. But remove the sick ape, and 'out of sight, out of mind' would rule with shocking suddenness and completeness. As for sexual reactions, there is no truer way of putting it than crudely: it is the wrong end, often the highly coloured wrong end, in which the male ape or monkey is interested.

Sex is not a joy to the other Primates; it is either an obsession or a tool in the satisfying of their needs. Perhaps therefore we may take in this respect a cheerful view of man's evolution: the power to see in the mind's eye may have emancipated him from brutishness and brought, whatever else it brought, much joy. Surely we can see no earthly reason why Neanderthaler, if not Pithecanthropus, should not have known what it was to be *in love*. He knew the moon and the beauty of the moon, and these undoubtedly better than we do. He knew how to show off and to court—and she knew how to be courted. Both sexes knew how to sing and dance—if for no better reason than that men and women possessed good vocal chords and highly mobile limbs.

Finally if 'conceptual-minded' man was very aware of love and life he must also have been aware of death. Surprisingly the other Primates show no real sign of this capability. The mother baboon will go on hugging her dead baby, not through excess of sentiment but rather it would seem as an instinctive reaction to something small and furry—she will go on until it is a limp rag. The female baboon who, as we learnt, may be fought over until her death, is not then abandoned. The animals in fact, all of them, have in this matter, both literally and colloquially, no idea. The Neanderthal Man certainly had an idea of death; it may have been one of the first ideas to get under his skin and to plague and worry him. If that is so there must have existed earlier and developing glimmerings of awareness throughout the many millenia of half-man's development. There is no physical trace of this—except possibly one. In some of the Pithecanthropine skulls the *foremen magnum*, the hole at the base of the skull, is enlarged. This is the cannibal's way of getting at the brains. Now cannibals seldom if ever practise their nauseous occupation from an unmixed motive of greed and hunger; there is rather an element of awe and superstition about it and an eating of the brains in order to acquire the strength and wisdom of the dead. That may surely have been the reason among the half-men, if they were addicted to the practice at all—and it is better to have had a spiritual reason for it, however misplaced and distorted, than a purely gastronomical one.

As for the Neanderthaler, there is one instance of possible evidence for the same practice. There is better foundation for speculation in the discovery of many true and proper burials of their dead. The body lies, perhaps in a corner of the cave, restricted into the position in which an unborn babe rests in the womb; and with it lie the remains of food. That scene may shadow forth either solicitude for the dead or fear of the dead; it may or may not show a belief in

The 'foetus' burial

an after life. But it does show unmistakably the existence in the mind of Neanderthal Man of the concept of death.*

What that concept meant in the way of the beginnings of dreams and imaginings and superstitions and symbolisms we will leave to a later chapter. Here we are only concerned with the development from an animal consciousness to a human one. In those very early men that came before *Homo sapiens* there was developing a mind that was both teachable and being taught, that was expanding the first early powers of conceptual thinking so that it could grapple with the problems of living both purely practical and, in a way of beginning, spiritual.

So at least it is reasonable to suppose. Yet in all this one thing, it must be obvious, is missing. How could early man have achieved

* The 'foetus' position may in particular mean much or nothing. Would man have known how the unborn babe lay—except perhaps by analogy with the beasts he hunted and dismembered?

what has been listed here without the aid of the power of speech? The answer must be that he could not. Much no doubt can be done by the aid of expression—those eyes again—of gesture and emotional cries. But conceptual thinking *demands* speech, demands the formulation of ideas into words so that the ideas may be communicated. Speech had to come—and it did. Not, greatly, with small-brained Pithecanthropus; that is why no doubt his 'culture' of flint making (and so his way of life) remained almost static for such an incredibly long time. But big-brained if wrong-shape-brained Neanderthal Man had surely enough of a frontal area for him to have evolved a language. It may not have been much of a one; he may, indeed he must, have found the job very difficult; but a language of sorts he surely possessed. When we have watched his retreat and the advance of the final inheritors of the earth, early *Homo sapiens*, we will return to language.

8

The Inheritors

THE discovery in 1868 of five skeletons in the Rock Shelter of Cro-Magnon (in that same Vézère valley in the Dordogne of Southern France where so much else was found) has been described as the uncovering of the first murder mystery. These five—three men, a woman and her child—lying with their tools and amulets, had obviously been done to death. The imaginative have suggested that here was a deed of revenge, and that the perpetrators were men of the Neanderthal race.

Such men would at least have had a motive. For the records do show a complete break, both in type of skeleton and type of tool; and the assumption must be that the new people, who were of our own species, *Homo sapiens*, did oust from their home in Europe these 'extreme' Neanderthal men. They did not, it seems, absorb them, intermarry with them, as is the frequent habit of conquerors. Once maybe the two kinds of men had had a common ancestor; but now the divergence was too great, and the invaders must have regarded the brutish shambling people that they found with fear and loathing—it has even been suggested that here lies the origin of the ogre in the story book.

How the ogre regarded his taller, handsomer, cleverer and more efficient rival it is impossible to say. It may not have been with hatred, but rather with a pathetic envy and a kind of jealous worship. That is an idea developed with much brilliant and sensitive imagination by William Golding in his novel *The Inheritors*.[11] The 'inheritors' are of course the invaders, the new men, who were truthfully to inherit the earth. The little band of Neanderthalers, trekking back in the spring to their usual haunts, gets wind of the interlopers. They suffer from them and are afraid, watch them and are fascinated;

finally die from them, with the exception of one little babe who is kept by the arrogant newcomers as a sort of half-animal pet. So, or in some such way, it must have been.

The natural question is, whence did this suddenly appearing and full-fledged *Homo sapiens* arrive? The stock answer has been 'somewhere in Southern Asia'; but with the comparatively recent discoveries elsewhere of 'generalized' Neanderthalers and of even more nearly *sapiens*-type human remains—in Cyrenaica, Sudan, Kenya, Tanganyika, Rhodesia—the more likely answer may well be 'somewhere in Africa'. These true men migrated perhaps during a warm spell in the last glaciation, round about thirty thousand years ago or more, and, like the Neanderthalers before them, they stayed when the climate grew colder again. They did not endure the cold for so many generations nor in quite such intensity; they arrived better equipped to withstand it. Unlike the Neanderthaler therefore they conquered their environment and their environment did not change or conquer them.

We will in this chapter survey 'Upper Paleolithic Man', the first clearly appearing man of undoubtedly our own species; we will survey him from the material angle only and over the period, probably something between five hundred and a thousand generations, when there was as yet no hint that the hard climate in which they thrived would ever disappear. This is a long space of time and we, from our artificial environment that will not stay still for a moment, cannot visualize or understand such changelessness. But compared with the long reign of the hand-axe this is little more than an interlude; we at last come to think in terms of tens of thousands of years and not hundreds.

The complicated and ever-changing nomenclature of this period need not worry us unduly—and that is a true and not merely a comforting sentiment. The three main cultures with which we are concerned, that is to say ways of life as illustrated by the tools and artifacts left behind, are Aurignacian, Solutrean and Magdalenian. It is, as we shall see, a sort of sandwich. How much these divisions denote divisions of racial stock or merely of changing use of tools it is impossible to say, still less so with the further sub-divisions that are made—that is why, for a general understanding, they are unimportant. However, lest the reader in consulting other books should become confused it ought to be recorded here that the Aurignacian suffers much mutilation. Here are the old and new sub-divisions of the culture:

Lower Aurignacian: now Chatelperronian ⎤ Sometimes
Middle Aurignacian: now Aurignacian ⎱ called, as a
Upper Aurignacian: now Gravettian ⎰ whole, Peri-
⎦ gordian.

Let us stick to simple Aurignacian. It is an easy and pleasant-sounding word. Those five victims in the rock shelter of Cro-Magnon—it is where a hotel bathroom now stands they say—were Aurignacians. Is this confusing? Not really; it is a matter of what was discovered first in this teeming limestone valley of the Dordogne.

What Cro-Magnon man may
have looked like

Aurignac skeletons were found in 1852, and there were as many as seventeen of them. *Aurignacian* then has been taken as the generic title: the Cro-Magnards are Aurignacian but not all Aurignacians are Cro-Magnard.

Not by a long way in fact: at Grimaldi in Italy were found Aurignacian remains, and one of the skulls *might* have belonged to a negro. But more of that later when at the end of the book we tackle the ticklish subject of Race.

What were, typically, these Aurignacian remains, and what was the typical Aurignacian like to look at? In fact what was it that they had that the Neanderthalers had not? The answer is shortly, better tools and better brains—and the second is the more outstanding. Indeed it is not only brain that is better but physique generally. These first-appearing undoubted specimens of our race were in a

96

heroic mould, not something patronizingly to look down upon but enviously to admire. They were usually over six feet in height; the brain case was often bigger than ours; the shambling gait of the Neanderthaler had completely gone, the penthouse ridge above the eyes nearly gone. The forehead was high and broad, the cheek-bones prominent, the chin good and strong.

As for tools there is shown now more inventiveness and more variety, as we should expect. The Neanderthaler's 'mousterian' flints, though not so clumsy as the hand-axe, being if you remember flakes off the central core and not the core itself, were comparatively shapeless things, most useful one would imagine as skin-scrapers and wood-whittlers. The Aurignacian, by more careful choosing and

Aurignacian flints: knife and
engraver (burin)

planning before the job started and by much more delicate pressure
—the mere hitting of one flint with another to produce an edge had gone long ago—produced genuine blades. They were straight or curved or pointed as he wanted them. They were essentially knives, chisels, engravers, the engravers or 'burins' being of various speci-alized shapes, such as the type found in the Cro-Magnon cave which was christened *burin busqué* and had a sort of crooked and pointed nose. But, what is more important, the true men were doing some-thing that the Neanderthalers never seem to have begun to do. This was not merely to use bone and tusk and antler but to make bone and horn and ivory tools. These are not materials easy to work—it was one of the ways in which the Piltdown skull hoaxers betrayed them-selves, by making and 'planting' a bone tool that was not and could not have been made by flint. But the Aurignacians managed a great deal, and the Magdalenians were even more successful after them.

Typically the Aurignacians made bone pins—skin clothes were being fastened together?—and spear points split at the end to take the wooden handle, the first appearance of hafting.

We spoke of the Solutreans being as it were a sandwich between the other two. This is largely true since the Magdalenian culture is very like the Aurignacian, whereas the Solutrean is widely different. It shows little evidence of bone work, but the flint work is marvellous. To say that there are no moderns to master the ultra-delicate pressure work that produced their 'laurel leaf' weapon-tips is perhaps obvious; but even no Stone Age work excels it, except per-

Solutrean flints: fine, delicate flaking. A laurel-leaf
point and a borer or drill

haps the much later efforts to rival and copy bronze. For the rest however the Solutreans, with little artistic ability, seem a rather dull and unimaginative people. They were great horse-hunters and seem to have spread west from the plains of Hungary. They either exterminated or drove out or absorbed or were partly absorbed by the Aurignacians—and then in turn their culture is replaced by the Magdalenians. Extermination is very unlikely; more probably a part of the Aurignacians moved out, retained and enlarged their skills—and came back as those that we have christened Magdalenians.

The Magdalenians were great workers in bone. They invented the needle—the *sewing* of clothes had come. They also carved out some beautiful barbed harpoons, probably for hunting rather than fishing. They produced from reindeer antler curious curved affairs a little like a boomerang that the first puzzled discoverers called non-committally *bâtons de commandement*; they had a hole through their broadest part and were probably used to straighten wooden spears. One other invention they made to help them in their hunting, and that was a spear-thrower, still used by primitive peoples. A long stick has a thick and notched end, into which the spear is

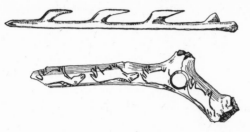

Magdalenean bone tools: harpoon and etched 'baton' or spear-straightener

fitted. Holding the other end the hunter obtains a wider arc and so a great acceleration to his throw. There is here really the first machine, applying the laws of dynamics to increase the natural power of the arm.

So much for the Aurignacians, the Solutreans, and the Magdalenians, as such. We are in danger of becoming swamped in detail and failing to gain a general picture of these peoples who had come to live and thrive in a long, broad belt to the south of the ice. The

Multiplying the power of the arm: spear-thrower

preceding paragraph gives the clue to the essential description of them. They *hunted*.

They were not the first to do that of course; man for a long time had graduated from a semi-vegetarian food gatherer and picker up of carnivore's unconsidered trifles to a preyer on the beasts. But these people did it so much more successfully with their better weapons. They did it, one must imagine, so much more actively: no longer the hanging on to the edge of the herd for the feeble or the

99

unlucky straggler, no longer the merely hopeful trap; but the bold *hunt*, even as time went on the planned and organized *battue*. The herds were still prolific and plentiful—reindeer and mammoth on the tundra, horse and bison and auroch (large and now extinct cattle, *Bos taurus primogenius*) on the steppes. Man, over the continuing centuries, was taking his golden opportunity.

Nor must we imagine his life as too forbiddingly hard. Hard it was—character forming. But he possessed the wide sweep of Europe-Asia for his hunting ground; and this he used, not surely hugging the ice more than was necessary—and even the tundra, though it is mere temporarily unfrozen earth, does produce a lovely and heartening spring and a warm if short summer. Man was indeed Cave Man; but when the greenness came he left his cave, and ate enormously and lived abroad. We find evidence of the successful and of the *organized* hunt: enormous piles of horse bones left by the Solutreans, careful piles left by the later Aurignacians of the bones of mammoth, tusks on *this* pile, hip-bones (these even helped to make huts of sorts) on *that*.

But there was the winter. What did paleolithic *Homo sapiens* do in the winter? He ousted the hyena and the great cave bear and sometimes the greater blood-sucking sabre-toothed tiger from the limestone caves, and he lit and tended his fires. He let his imagination loose, and dreamt of animals and the fertility of animals and of wives and mothers and mother-figures. He modelled mother-figures. With his burins he engraved animals on his spear-throwers and spear-straighteners, even on any odd bit of bone.

He also drew and painted on the walls of caves.

That of course is what Upper Paleolithic Man is famous for and will remain famous for. Not only does he appear full-fledged man but before his time is out full-fledged artist. Always however, or nearly always, artist portraying animals. That is the thing to understand: these mighty hunters lived with, and upon, great beasts; they 'lived' animals. In a striking phrase of H. G. Wells' in his *Outline of History*,[12] 'they watched and drew and killed and ate'.

Utter savages though they may have been—painted as well as panting savages—they could not have done all these things successfully if they had not had by now, to help direct their activities, to release and stimulate their imaginations, a speech that was fully entitled to be called a language.

100

9

The Birth of Language

CHARLES DARWIN, to whom much must be forgiven considering how little of our present knowledge was at his disposal, insisted that nothing fundamentally differentiated man from the beasts, not even the possession of language. He has been severely criticized since. For once he was not right; but his mistake has left its mark.

If we were asked to name the three inventions that did most to take life over the threshold into a new world we should do well I think to choose fire, tools and speech—and to give the prize to speech. Nor is human speech something that developed out of animal noises in the same sort of way that a fire develops out of an ember, by means of a little coaxing. It is a genuinely new invention. What is more, it is an invention that, as we said in an earlier chapter, *had* to come. It had to come, given man's intelligence and powers of conceptual thinking. We shall do well to look for a moment at what is called 'animal language' and again at animal intelligence.

Darwin cites with approval the four or five different kinds of barks that his dog could make and the fact that it started hunting around if one cried in an eager voice, 'Hi, hi, where is it?' He also quotes with pride the fact that an earlier dog of his recognized him after his return from the voyage round the world in the *Beagle*, a matter of five years and two days. We are with him all the way—until he comes to his conclusions. We may even remind ourselves of a more touching feat of memory, that Argus, Odysseus' dog, recognized him, according to Homer—and why should we not believe it? —after an absence of twenty years and in spite of the wily old man's disguise as a beggar.

But what of all this? Is it, as Darwin wished to persuade us,

101

the beginning of language and in particular the display of a conceptual intelligence that with but a little coaxing, if we only knew the right formula, would result in speech? Or is it rather a display on the one part of an extensive emotional repertoire and on the other of a fidelity and sensitivity towards man and an emotional dependence on him that causes the dog's brain to be imprinted with a memory that is virtually indelible?

Richard Wilson's book *The Miraculous Birth of Language*[13] helps to give the answer. The author sets his argument in terms of awareness of time and space; he writes:

> While it is clear that the [Odysseus'] dog has some kind of memory, and hence some grasp of time within his own physical life span, it is equally clear, so far as can be discovered, that the dog has no sense of time prior to his own birth or subsequent to his own death. He has no sense or consciousness of any dog's life of a hundred years ago. He could not be awakened to any consciousness of or interest in the story of Darwin's dog, nor could Darwin's dog have been awakened to an interest in the dog of Odysseus. . . . His mind is enveloped and confined by time within the short span of his own physical life.
>
> Man's mind, on the other hand, though centred in a material body like the dog's, has broken through this envelope or sense-barrier of time, and holds all time now in its grasp instead of being held by it. It has no more difficulty in holding Homer's story of three thousand years ago than Darwin's of a hundred years ago, and it explicitly differentiates the stretch of time between the two events. To all this past time the dog's mind is stone-dead.

Professor Wilson advances similarly the argument that the dog has no awareness of space other than the space immediately about him. 'While he remains in Vancouver'—the professor is a Canadian—'his mind cannot be awakened to any sense or consciousness of a dog show in Montreal.' To a man on the contrary 'all points are merely differentiations of a single space *which he holds within his mind* as an always-present mental world'—the italics are mine. The ardent pet lover may of course resent this belittlement, as he may regard it, of the intelligence of the dog—'Let us be fair,' he may say, 'the dog hasn't got words to describe to himself other places and other times!' Which is of course the point.

It is the point, and for this simple reason: animals have not got the words because they do not feel the need for the words. The dog, as Professor Wilson says, could not be 'awakened to any interest' in the story of another dog remote in space and time: he has not that sort of brain.

We can now stop thinking in terms of space and time, which is Professor Wilson's particular way of putting it, to the way of putting it in Chapter 7 of this book: the absence or presence of the power of 'conceptual thinking'. In other words, the animal's concept, or idea of anything, stretches so little way beyond the here and now.

Now what have we proved, and what are we seeking to prove? We have I think established additional evidence for one of the two truths which are as it were the twin pillars of this book: 'man is an animal; but man is much more than an animal'—in this instance the second truth. But we are concerned now with the birth of language. What we have so far established is that man and man only has the kind of intelligence that *demands* a language. We find it hard to realize this, knowing as we do how intelligent animals can often be. But if an animal's physiological make-up is such that a new characteristic could not be properly used that characteristic will never be developed. Hours, days, weeks have been spent trying to teach the most intelligent ape to talk: result, after patient physical manipulation of the lips he will say 'Mama'—and never trouble unless he is encouraged to use his marvellous acquisition again. There is here a barrier which no animal passes.

Now, therefore, to go to the reverse of the picture, let us try hard to think without the aid of words. A good deal is possible: we summon up pictures. But even when we 'daydream' we soon break into words in our minds. Or try something else: imagine directing someone to a task without the benefit of words. 'Go and get the new meat axe!' Without words we should either have to go through an elaborate pantomime, with doubtful success, or do the job ourselves. But with words it is easy. We have given names to the things.

Given names: that you will remember in the legend of Genesis is what God allowed Adam to do. It is a very significant, a very impressive thing to do—the impressiveness of it undoubtedly struck the primitive men who did it. It gives *power*—though perhaps not always in the way that primitive man imagined, which is a point we shall return to later. It was also a difficult thing to do. Let us now turn to considering how in fact language was invented.

Anyone of course can give a name to a thing. The trouble is that all your companions have got to agree to your naming; it needs to be a convention that everyone will accept. A *convention* it is, do not forget that: something artificial, something purely in the mind's eye, a symbol, *and* a symbol that tacitly and by use is accepted by the community as 'meaning' a certain thing. A conventionalized symbol used within the mind for the material object or action without: that is a word.

How it all started it is not easy to see. There have been many guesses, and not all of them good. An extension of the natural emotional cries of the animal seems an obvious possibility. But it is not a likely one. One can imagine the women of the clan wailing and keening over a death and some such word as 'woe!' arriving. But little else: a shriek of terror remains a shriek of terror, and no more, to this day. We shall get nowhere on those lines.

One favourite suggestion is the onomatopoeic, sometimes called disrespectfully the 'bow-wow' theory: you name a thing after the sound that it makes or that you feel it makes. That is why we call a plover a peewit. But why a swan or a robin—for that matter why a plover? Obviously it would be ridiculous to try to make such a theory stretch all the way.

There is however an extension of it that may be a little more fruitful. It has been noted that in many languages the trilled 'r' for instance occurs in words delineating motion, such as 'running' or a 'rill', and that abrupt actions are given words with abrupt consonants—'stop!' It is very possible that people trying to invent words that conveyed the right idea to the listener would as it were gesticulate with their mouths, that they would twist the mouths and manipulate the vocal organs to suit: 'a *t*ee*n*y-*wee*ny mouse met an e*nor*mous lion'. In fact you can take it a little further back: the gesticulating expression would be no more than a copy, an unconscious copy no doubt, of the descriptive gesticulation that the whole body was making. Communication of ideas, that is to say

104

'speech', by dance and gesticulation is not at all impossible—the bees do it—though it does not get you very far. (Deaf and dumb language is an artificial affair invented *after*, and because of, articulate speech and writing.) That does not say however that at first the two did not run together, articulate speech as a refinement and an aid—a pretty necessary aid one would think—to the gesticulatory language of dance.

Another possibility, not wholly unallied, is that much of speech came from singing, not so much that wailing we talked about as from a sort of careless, cheerful, childish exercise of the larynx. After all, the human animal has a very good larynx, and if he can make a remarkable variety of noises, and noises that his companion may think pleasant, then he will certainly make them. All languages are full of nonsense rhymes and repetitives—dimble-damble, pitter-patter, with a hey nonny no! It is not too fanciful to imagine the spell-binder of the clan—the volatile person, the wit, the jester, or the shower-off—standing and delivering a glorious rigmarole of sound, to the amazement and gratification of the listeners, and meaning?—perhaps a little. Nor is it too fanciful to imagine the arrival from all that, after many repetitions no doubt, as a drop of scent is distilled from a thousand rose leaves, of one or two real words.

This is a pleasant idea, put forward by the Danish philologist and grammarian Otto Jespersen in his book *Language*.[14] We may follow him further:

> 'Suppose some dreaded enemy has been defeated and slain; the troop will dance round the dead body and strike up a chant of triumph, say something like "tarara-boom-de-ay!" This combination of sounds, sung to a certain melody, will now easily become what might be called a proper name for that particular event; it might be roughly translated, "The terrible foe from beyond the river is slain" or "We have killed the dreadful man from beyond the river" or "Do you remember when we killed him?" or something of the same sort. Under slightly altered circumstances it may become the proper name of the man who slew the enemy.'

'Old Tarara' in fact. On an analogy with the Earl of Sandwich

105

or Lord Cardigan it might become the name of his favourite food or piece of apparel.

It is probably however the verb rather than the noun that is the first essential. We must not seek to put language on too exalted a plane from the start. *Doing things* simply cries out for language, doing things together. The imperative arrives:

'Tote that barge, lift that bale!'

Or in paleolithic terms, the youngster being taught the precious art of making flint axes, 'Hold it lightly!—hit it gently!—move that finger!'—much gesture but ably supplemented by talk. From that someone takes the big step to the story, the narration—from the imperative mood to the past tense and the imperfect. 'Your venerable grandfather (salute his spirit!) never held his knapper like that; he always said . . .' Or, in an even more practical situation, 'Beware that cave, for yesterday I entered and found a lion in it and the lion nearly got me before I escaped.' That is an excellent use for language that any animal might envy.

Nevertheless, for language to achieve this power to describe the *imagined* scene rather than the here-and-now must have been a very difficult achievement and not an early one. Just as the animal seems hardly able to envisage anything more than that here-and-now, so the early and unpractised brain must have found it hard to find words for it. It needs not only an elaboration of tense but of pronouns: having with difficulty and triumph really distinguished between *I, you* and *him*, one now has to conceive *this* and *that*: '*this* by me now; *that* belonging to the other fellow I was talking about—no, you can't see it!' William Golding in *The Inheritors* makes his poor bewildered Neanderthalers hesitate when they seek to describe the past. They hold their heads in an agony of concentration and begin portentously, 'I see a picture!' That is a good touch.

We can sometimes go for corroboration of our guesses to the languages of extant primitive peoples. In his book *Aspects of Language*[15] Professor Entwistle tells us that to the Kwakintl Indian of North America such a simple sentence as 'the farmer kills the duck' would be unintelligible. It would have to be something like 'the farmer, invisible to us but standing behind a door not far away from me, you being seated well out of reach, kills that duckling that belongs to you'. The here-and-now, the concrete, the speaker and the hearer, have to be brought in. Even the noun itself is not always simple, suffering complication from the superior need and obviousness of the verb: the Arunta language (of the Stone Age Australian aborigines) has for 'man' a word meaning '*being more*', that is being superior, or superior being. Indeed that seems the most probable aspect of primitive languages, their *creakiness*. They became stiff and cumbersome and over-complicated at once— Professor Entwistle in the book already mentioned talks of early language 'pululating genders, numbers, moods, tenses and cases'. Complicated they were and yet at the same time inadequate. Here is the lament of Father Jacob Baegert who nearly two hundred years ago sought to convert the now extinct Californian Indians:

'The Waicuri language is of an exceedingly barbarous and rude description . . . the great deficiency of language consists in the total absence of a great many words, the want of which would seem to render it almost impossible for reasonable beings to converse with each other and to receive instruction in the Christian religion. For whatever is not substantial, and cannot be seen or touched or otherwise perceived by the senses, has no name in the Waicuri language. There are no nouns whatever for expressing virtues, vices, or the different dispositions of the mind, and there exist only a few adjectives of this class, namely *merry*, *sad*, *lazy* and *angry*, all of which merely denote such humours as can be perceived in a person's face. . . . They have particular words for signifying *an old man*, *an old woman*, *a young man*, *a young woman*, and so forth; but the terms *old* and *young* do not exist in their language.'*

This last is a frequent comment upon primitive languages, that with the lack of words for generalized or immaterial things there goes what seems to us a plethora of terms for the touched and seen: every kind of tree will have its name—and the learner will be expected to remember them!—but there may be no word for 'tree'; no word for a 'relative' but separate words for maternal uncle and paternal uncle and many more distant relationships, and even perhaps a different word for a thing when it belongs to you and when it belongs to your mother-in-law. . . .

* Quoted by Mr. Leslie Paul in his book *Nature into History*.[16]

107

So then must the first languages have grown up; such inadequacies and excesses they must have possessed. But note that we say languages not language. Each tribe, each community, will invent its own. And what is more important, its language will fit that community, as a glove fits a hand; it will reflect exactly, in what it includes and what it leaves out, in where it is poor and where it is rich, the society who invented it and the demands that it made upon the spoken word as it did so.

The demands of Pithecanthropus would be very small indeed. Whether in fact he talked at all is questionable, though the anthropologists consider his brain to have been just sufficiently developed. What is likely is that his way of life did, very gradually, develop within him the power of speech: we have seen that it is very much what is demanded that is produced. Slowly the hand-axe user must have become a word user. But the progress besides being slow must never have been very great, for otherwise the culture of Lower Paleolithic Man would have advanced further than it did.

That indeed is the great truth, that advance in culture and in speech will go together, each calling forth the other and neither being possible alone. The creature who can clearly remember the past and imagine the future will develop the power of speech, so that he may communicate with his fellow beings and improve his own powers of thought in the process. The creature capable of conceptual thinking will develop words to clothe his concepts. And once he has done so his powers are increased beyond telling: society is possible, the inner life is possible.

Speech in fact creates a second world, the inner immaterial world to match the outer and material. Do not let us belittle the achievement from having considered its early inadequacies. With the power of speech, of thinking in speech and of communicating with his fellows in speech, man becomes by that single invention a new and different creature. He is marked off from the beast; he becomes a spiritual being.

And with that last adjective in mind let us for a moment think back to what has been said, by Father Baegert for instance. That there were no words adequate to express the concepts of Christianity was no doubt true; but there may well, on the other hand, have been words adequate for such religion and ceremonies as the Waicuri Indians possessed and observed, which words would no doubt pass the earnest Father by: early languages would not long in fact remain solely material and concrete, and of the here-and-now.

Man now had a tool *for his imagination*, a tool for pushing out into the open all the feelings and emotions of his human and pre-human nature. These will neither be simple nor always rational, nor always pleasant—not even always pleasant for himself. But he will undoubtedly persist.

10

The Flowering of Art

I N TERMS of that allegory which we should not despise, man and woman, their restless nature having goaded them to seek understanding rather than to remain innocent, have been turned out of the Garden of Eden. They are no longer in a state of nature; they have in the realm of the spirit completely shed their animal skin; they are 'as gods, knowing good and evil'. Speech they possess to give clothing to their imagination; the eye to see with; and their birthright of the clever hand.

Now, so long as we remember to remain humble and avoid becoming dogmatic, doctrinaire and opinionated, we can by taking thought penetrate some way into the mind of man.* Intuition will help us; so too will the findings of psychologists, and philosophers, and anthropologists reporting on the ways of primitives still extant. But our greatest guide, to which we must always return wherever possible, which must govern by its absence as well as its presence, is what man has physically left behind him: his tools, his rubbish dumps and his deserted hearths, the occasional evidence of burial and other rites, his modelling and carving in miniature, his painting on rocks and in the fastnesses of caves.

It is his art and in particular his cave art that brings man closest to us. It is so personal; it appeals to our imagination.

Not so easily however does it appeal to our understanding; and that is something that we must try to make it do. The first necessity is to know exactly what we are talking about, to review and analyse what has been found. This the present chapter will

---

* Except where the context seems to make some distinction necessary, we shall talk simply of 'man', meaning early man, Stone Age Man. At present, and for the next four chapters, we are still with Upper Paleolithic Man or man at the end of the Old Stone Age.

seek to do: some factual reporting on Lascaux and Altamira and the rest—after, that is to say, a paragraph or two where we shall consider that rather portentous word 'art' and try to come to terms with it.

If we are not careful we may let the artist, or rather the talker-about-art—they are not necessarily separate persons—frighten us into muddled thinking if not an actual inferiority complex about art. When about eighty years ago cave paintings were first discovered and publicized, Paleolithic Man being found, as Geoffrey Bibby has put it,[10] 'with a palette and paint brush in his hand', the first re-action was one of amazement and disbelief. This may have been partly caused by the Darwin-Piltdown complex as one might call it, which was still leading people to visualize the maker of the most excellent flint tools to be a somewhat humanized chimpanzee. But it was not wholly that; there was the other complex, the inferiority one, already working. 'What, cave man an *artist*?' The truth is of course, as we have said many times before, that man has imagination and supremely skilful hands which he is aching to use, if only he can find the time and excuse for doing so. The skill of the paleolithic artists is extraordinary and surprising, so too are some of the surfaces on which they chose to scratch and draw and paint; but that they should have chosen to do so at all is not in the least sur-prising. If we see vividly we want to portray vividly; and some of us in all ages will be able, and encouraged, to do so.

Not only that, but it is the property of men, for which we may be duly thankful, to love to exert their skill and to do a job as well as can be done—often better than strictly utilitarian requirements dictate. That is something we have already noticed as apparent in the making of flints. It applies to the making of practically all things throughout the ages, an almost universal habit that is only broken with the machine and the industrial age. Nowadays we tend to be surprised if a thing is beautiful and has had loving care ex-pended upon it, and say with awe and surprise that it is 'artistic'. Let us forget the word, since it tends to raise the wrong sort of feeling within us. Of course man is an artist, and has been so since hand and eye were vivified by imagination. But being an artist, though it may have helped him gradually to become something more, did not prevent Paleolithic Man from being still a savage. . . .

Our dogs, one might say, have been the great cave discoverers. The existence of both the Altamira and Lascaux caves were first made known by the excited yelpings of questing dogs who had fallen through and couldn't get out.

It was the Altamira dog who first fell through, in 1868. Altamira is twenty miles from Santander on the north coast of Spain, at the eastern end of the Cantabrian mountains. It was the local land-owner and amateur geologist, Don Marcelino de Santuola, who somewhat tardily followed up the trail. And it was his daughter of twelve, Maria—the tale is well known but too pleasant to be omitted

The final accomplishments of cave art: four beasts from Altamira

—who, being smaller and so the more easily able to look up at the low ceiling, first discovered the painted bulls, *'Papa, papa, mira, toros pintados!'* Don Marcelino, and his helpers and champions, then spent years persuading the experts that the paintings were neither by the local artist who had been commissioned to copy them, nor by Roman soldiers, nor by anybody else than the Magdalenian cave men who had lived nearby some fifteen to twenty thousand years ago.

Lascaux was found and explored sixty-one years later, in 1940, and the dog owners this time were four boys of fifteen years or so. Fortunately they were intelligent and educated and enthusiastic boys, and they and their schoolmaster guarded the cave until the experts could come along to inspect. Nor of course were these later experts sceptical. They were led by the greatest of them all, the Abbé Breuil, and the analysis was immediately thorough. These paintings are held to be by the Magdalenian's predecessors and probable cousins, the Aurignacians—Lascaux being in the same valley of the Vézère where lies Cro-Magnon.

Lascaux and Altamira are the greatest and most famous of the painted caves. An exhaustive list of them would contain over a hundred names; a map in the beautiful book of photographs and description by Fernand Windels, *The Lascaux Cave Paintings*,[17] shows thirty-three important sites. These are mainly in three clumps, around Altamira in Cantabria, around Aurignac on the north slopes of the Pyrenees, and around the famous Vézère valley in the Dordogne. A few are in Switzerland, and one so far found in Italy.

First let us quote from an unemotional description, that of the late Mr. Windels of the entrance into Lascaux[17]:

'There were a few yards of rubble, slipping away under one's feet, and to the right a short gallery, damp and bare, which has now been partly stopped up; then, ahead, there opened out the Main Chamber of the cave. It is an oval, 100 feet by 33 and about 20 feet high, with a slight slant carrying on the line of the entrance.

And there, as though filing past in weird games of follow-my-leader, are gigantic oxen, horses and deer. Reds, blacks, and yellows, on the fine crystalline "skin" which gives a varnished appearance to the rock, seem in some places as fresh as though they had been painted twenty years ago. You go on, avoiding the puddles which dot the surface of the ground, and out of the confusion of this extraordinary mass the animals become distinguishable one by one. First of all, on the left appears the first picture of the cave, the black head of a horse. Next comes a fantastic animal of thick-set proportions, with a short snout, a coat dappled with round spots, and a brow which seems to bear two enormous horns; on a lower level several black horses run on round the flat of the wall. . . . You then come to two enormous bulls outlined in black; they are over 13 feet in length and face one another, making a frame for a set of five little red, black and yellow deer.'

113

Such is the impression: a conglomeration, rich, realistic, impressive. (More incidentally of the 'fantastic animal' later.) How was it all done?

The oyster shells that Don Marcelino de Santuola was grubbing up while his daughter saw the bulls gives the answer: earths—to be more specific oxides of iron (ochre) and manganese—ground to a powder, occasionally blown on to a prepared surface but more often mixed with fat or water or urine (as some primitives do now, a labour-saving device perhaps?) and then packed into the oyster shell as a container and applied with stick or brush or (for large surfaces) perhaps with a pad of lichen or moss.

In the method and style of painting there must have been a slowly growing tradition; a tradition that the pupil-artist, the neophyte, undoubtedly had to learn, and an historical sequence. The beginnings seem to have been lines made with the fingers where the walls were soft, first meandering then taking form. With these went the mark of hands, either dipped in paint or outlined in paint by spray. Later there may have been something in the way of the artist's signature, 'this day have I set my hand . . .'; but at first these had other significances, as we shall see in the following chapter. There follows delineation in outline, in wider outline, in one colour, light and shade, and finally, as at Altamira, in a combination of colours. There is also much engraving on cave walls—this more difficult to be seen and photographed by the modern intruder—and sometimes a combination of engraving and painting. At Lascaux the black of an old painting is used to achieve what the modern artist would call a scraper-board effect. Very often the artist has taken advantage of the contours of the cave wall or ceiling to add to his painting an effect of bas relief, the contours having no doubt provided the original idea for the painting.

All of that may sound very modern and efficient and completely understandable. Let us record some other facts.

The animals depicted are only occasionally the enemies of man, almost always the food of man. At Font de Gaume a statistical count has been made, giving an idea of relative importance: 80 bison, 40 horses, 23 mammoths, 17 reindeer, 8 wild cattle, 4 antelopes, 2 woolly rhinoceros, 1 bear, 1 wolf, 1 lioness. There is hardly ever any decoration or 'scenery'; no plants, at least none recognizable, and with an outstanding exception no birds. Then man himself is very seldom depicted. If so, he is either masked and disguised as an animal or is sketched in in a most formalized and conventionalized sort of way. In the Lascaux cave, in a most inaccessible spot, is a famous 'hunting scene' (to which we shall recur) where the man is a queer child's-sketch, with a face more like a bird's.

Here there is another strange fact to be noticed, that the paintings are often in most inaccessible places, where the artist must have had to be helped or held in position or furnished with some sort of scaffolding. Often too, what would seem much more accessible places are left entirely bare, whilst perversely the difficult canvas is used again. The re-use of space is a very frequent habit, whether from a sort of casualness or of set intent is not known, though it

'Tectiforms'—the unexplained. A 'blazon' from Lascaux
and a hut or trap from Font de Gaume

does seem possible that some duplications are contemporary and so of course intentional and with significance.

Next, there are quite a few scratchings or paintings that are seldom popularly reproduced because they are unspectacular but that are at the same time wellnigh inexplicable. There are twisted and wavy lines and dots and crosses; there are square grilles and parti-coloured oblongs given the names of 'blazons'; and contraptions looking like primitive huts, or igloos, given the non-committal name of *tectiforms*—'in the form of a building'.

Next point: the animals quite often appear to be pregnant, or else are shown with one or more darts or spears sticking into them.

Finally: not only are the paintings sometimes put in surprisingly inaccessible places, but the whole collection is usually difficult of access—*not* in caves that had been lived in. It is as if a picture gallery instead of being in Leicester Square were at the end of the Aldwych branch Tube line with a couple of hundred yards on the hands and knees at the end of it. The Cave of Combarelles has just that ending; Niaux's paintings are nearly half a mile within. And a cave is pitch dark. . . .

What all that leads to we will discuss in the next chapter. We will prepare the way for it however, and by another quotation, less factual but certainly not fanciful. It is from the pen of M. A.

Nightmare faces and figures from the caves of Altamira, Cabrerets and Les Combarelles

Leroi-Gourhan, sub-director of the Paris Musée de l'Homme, who writes in an introduction to Mr. Windel's book on Lascaux:

'. . . the caves have not changed, and whoever is familiar with their depths knows the range of the impressions that meet him there; the crushing stillness of the silence; the instinctive sinking of the voice till it ends by whispering; the sudden burst with which the atmosphere can be transformed by singing, making the decoration flash instantly out in detail as the hold of the dark vaults snaps away; and—then the silence falling once more at the end of the song, more tragic and more bodily than ever.'

11

Magic

Was the painted cave used, as M. Leroi-Gourhan seems obviously to suggest, as a sort of paleolithic cathedral? He is not the only one who suggests it. Altamira was almost at once christened 'The Sistine Chapel of Early Man'. Or is that all a romantic sentimentality? Was it not on the other hand all simple exuberance and *joie de vivre* and art for art's sake?—after all, man *likes* to paint. Or, if we will allow the caves a purpose, why should it not have been a severely practical purpose and a purpose practically carried out? We can for instance call those 'tectiforms' the delineation of animal traps, and those 'blazons' tribal emblems, very like army regimental or divisional badges. We could visualize a sort of 'briefing' before the hunt, with the equivalent of the efficient staff officer demonstrating just how to kill and where to kill and ending with a pep-talk on tribal unity and *esprit-de-corps*—'a happy tribe is an efficient tribe'.

That is not an entirely fantastic idea. But it is supremely unlikely to have happened; we are forgetting the characteristics of the early man.

Once more: his is a lately animal mind and an unpractised mind. It has as yet little, desperately little, accumulated knowledge of the world behind it. Man knows only himself; he is the self-conscious creature. He knows too that he wants things, wants so intensely things to happen or not to happen. He is a wilful creature. And he wants things so deeply because he can sit and think about them, visualize them, see them in the mind's eye. What is he going to do about it all?

Perhaps it is obvious to the reader that he is being led ever so gently, like a horse past the place where he shied last time, to a contemplation of 'magic'. The reader may never have shied for that matter. But it is easy to get a wrong impression of magic as understood by the primitive mind and to react unfavourably to an idea that may seem too facilely used. In particular we may perhaps instinctively react against the idea that the cave paintings were instruments of magic, because it seems to detract from the beauty and artistic merit of the pictures—or because we like to possess our own pet ideas on the subject. However, I think it is true that the more one thinks about the paintings the more one is driven back to 'magic' as the only explanation.

But not a black magic, not at all necessarily a sinister magic. The paintings were of serious intent undoubtedly, for animals and hunting were serious matters, but neither evil nor necessarily as we understand the word mysterious. Even possibly on occasion—this is admittedly a pet idea, but primitives are often brilliant mimics and appreciative audiences, witness Elenore Smith Bowen's *Return to Laughter*,[18] or Darwin's descriptions of the Fuegians—there may have been, amongst those allowed into the precincts, wild shouts of laughter. They would be soon dimmed no doubt, and they echoed rather terribly. More often there would be awed silence. Or impressive, thrilled dancing. Singing perhaps as M. Leroi-Gourhan suggests. Certainly burning desire and intense, if repressed, excitement—for man is an excitable animal.

We will now seek to understand what magic meant to the primitive mind, and then see how fittingly a practice of it would explain the painting of animals within the fastnesses of caves.

First, the practice of magic is something severely practical. It deals admittedly with what we should call the supernatural, but not what the primitive would call supernatural. Indeed that is the second point: he would not use the word at all, for in his mind there is no difference between natural and supernatural—he doesn't yet know how nature works.

But what he does know—as we have already suggested—is that he is terribly anxious to make it work *his* way. Are not we all that, is it not an inevitable consequence of the fact that we can think and imagine? If we worry about the future surely primitive man worried also: less complicatedly perhaps but hardly less intensely, considering that the contrary course of events meant to him not inconvenience, nor 'loss of income' nor 'such a nuisance' nor 'makes me look a fool', but only two things, starvation and death. How then to control nature? It is what we do by science. Primitive man does it by magic—to which should be added, to be fair to him, the self-confidence and assertive will-power that a belief in the efficacy of magic will engender.

Magic is based on one colossal misapprehension. It is a misinterpretation, a mixing up, of cause and effect. To help us understand, let us turn to Sir James Frazer's great collection and analysis of magic practices and much else, *The Golden Bough*[19]—it will not be the last time that we shall turn to that book. Frazer, a terrific worker right up to his death at eighty-seven, first published the book in 1890; it gave all the sources of his colossal collected evidence and finally ran to twelve volumes. He then brought out the more wieldy and better-known abridged edition in 1922. 'If,' he says in this:

'If we analyse the principles of thought on which magic is based, they will probably be found to resolve themselves into two: first, that like produces like, or that an effect resembles its cause; and, second, that things which have once been in contact with each other continue to act on each other at a distance after the physical contact has been severed. The former principle may be called the Law of Similarity, the latter the Law of Contact or Contagion. From the first of these principles, namely the Law of Similarity, the magician infers that he can produce any effect he desires merely by imitating it: from the second he infers that whatever he does to a material object will affect equally the person with whom the object was once in contact, whether it formed part of his body or not.

A little further on he continues:

'. . . the same principles which the magician applies in the practice of his art are implicitly believed by him to regulate the operations of inanimate nature; in other words, he tacitly assumes that the Laws of Similarity and Contact are of universal application and are not limited to human actions.'

In other words, that was how the world worked, and obviously you could do your bit to make it work the way you wanted. Let us look, with Frazer, at a few examples. If you are a woman and want to be a mother it will help if you make an image of a baby and hold it in your lap—so are said to believe the Bataks of Sumatra. If you live on fish as used the Nootka Indians to do, and the fish do not come in due season, your wizard will make an image of a fish and put it into the water in the direction from which the fish generally appear. If rain is wanted, he will ritually sprinkle water. If you have jaundice you may with luck transfer it to the sun which is bright yellow, or to a stone curlew, for he has a brilliant yellow eye. In Cheshire they used to cure warts by rubbing with bacon and inserting the bacon beneath the bark of an ash tree—the tree gets the knobs and you were made free of them. Or—and this is the usual example given and it is a good one—if you wish to harm a person you make a waxen image of him and stick pins or something equally unpleasant into his image: wherever you stick, your enemy will feel the harm and pain. Here is a world-wide belief. As a better example to our purpose, you may make up the image, if you can manage it, with something belonging to your enemy, best of all something that was once part of him such as his nail clippings or his hair: that will be doubly efficacious. Here you have a combination of the two 'laws', both of contagion and of similarity. The essence of primitive magic is that there is an influence, working across space and time, making use as we might say of an invisible and unexplained —but why seek to explain?—'ether'. There is always a 'sympathy' between the things that once touched or were all-of-a-piece, between the things that have similar properties or are made to have similar properties by mimicry or imitation.

Now how did all this come about? Why is it that people have been, as we should say, so silly? It is essential for our proper appreciation of the primitive mind that we should understand this, and particularly that we should realize that 'silly' is an unnecessarily harsh epithet. Mistaken, yes—though in practice it may have worked. Silly, no.

There are two ways of tackling this. The first is by comparison with ourselves. Do we not know of innumerable superstitions, and even practise some ourselves? For instance there are uncountable 'country' cures for warts, and all or nearly all based on sympathetic magic. It can be argued that in this sort of thing we are unaware that a magical element ever existed. But what of the belief, certainly not dead, that for a pregnant woman to see a hare is to give her baby a hare lip? What of all the belief in the 'influence' of the stars? For that matter, though on a different plane, what of that 'ether' which the scientists invented to explain how the sun's light reached us? We believed in it; but now the scientists begin to hold that belief as silly. We were not however silly at the time to believe: one must have some hypothesis to work upon and to accept, until a better one may prove it false. Primitive man was not different in this.

Sometimes the practices seem rather endearing to us as we read of them. The hunter of Cambodia, it is said, used sometimes, if his nets remained empty, to walk away and strip himself naked —he was now being an animal—and would then stroll back to the net and inadvertently get himself entangled in it, exclaiming in a surprised manner: 'Hello, what's this? I'm afraid I'm caught!' We can surely have some sympathy with this, can in fact almost see ourselves doing it—feeling a little foolish no doubt but telling ourselves that it *might* work, it might 'turn our luck'. Perhaps the Cambodian hunter felt something the same—and then, if still meeting with unsuccess, blamed his lack of faith. . . .

Then there is the Hindoo lover. 'The ancient books of the Hindoos,' reports Sir James Frazer, 'lay down a rule that after sunset on his marriage night a man should sit silent with his wife till the stars begin to twinkle in the sky. When the pole star appears, he should point it out to her, and, addressing the star, say, "Firm art thou; I see thee, the firm one. Firm be thou with me, O thriving one!" Then, turning to his wife, he should say, "To me Brihaspati has given thee; obtaining offsprings through me, thy husband, live with me a hundred autumns." '

The intention, Frazer points out, is plainly to guard against the fickleness of fortune and of humanity by virtue of the influence of that most steadfast of stars, which never changes its place. It is the same wish, he points out, as is expressed in Keats' last sonnet:

> Bright star! Would I were as steadfast as thou art—
> Not in lone splendour hung aloft the sky.

We are a long way now, no doubt, from primitive magic. But the connecting path is recognizable. Keats invokes the star that is symbolic of constancy. So does the Hindoo; though his is more than a poetic fancy, it is a pious hope for definite results. So too does the savage hunter, more crude and more practical, who eats, first and particularly, the brain of his quarry so that he may be endowed with its strength and wisdom. It is a matter of degree: there is a connection between magic and symbolism.

And symbolism means an enormous amount to the savage. Indeed it means an enormous amount to all of us: man lives and has always lived surrounded by symbolism. To use it is natural for his mind, perhaps essential. We invent blazons and coats of arms and badges and flags and respond impassionedly to the symbolism that they portray, or that we put on to them—and the flag incidentally is said* to derive from the umbilical cord, that used to flutter down in representation from one of the Egyptian processional standards: a most potent symbol of fertility and the continuity of life. Symbolism is a sort of shorthand, a method of implying much by very little. No wonder it is a trick of the mind. It is a trick of speech too, the most obvious way of coining metaphorical words, of speaking imaginatively and poetically: 'there is a fire in my heart, a frog in my throat, a mist before my eyes, a fluttering like of a captive linnet in my bowels, and my love for you is like . . . like . . . is like the constancy of the North Star.'

Nevertheless: that like should *produce* like is a far cry from all that. We have really in the end to give up in our attempt to understand the mentality of the users of magic. The best we can do is to see dimly, to realize that the thing is possible, is not fantastic. Man was ignorant, man was as a child; and like to like impressed him. Then, having been impressed, man's vivid, new, untrammelled imagination did the rest. Let us come back to the cave man and his paintings. But one word before we do that. There is this obvious question: if man believed in magic, why did he go on believing in it, for surely he would see that it did not work? The answer is partly our comment on the Cambodian hunter. If it does not work, then there is only one explanation: our magic—or the professional magician's magic—was not good enough; we must try again. Or, alternatively, it did work. It worked often just because the magic ceremony had endowed the participator with a self-assurance that commanded success—do not ignore that possibility. Then

* See Sir Grafton Elliot Smith's *Human History*.[20]

sometimes it was obviously going to work in any case: if the savage solemnly goes through a ritual for helping the sun in his difficult course, and behold the next day the sun does rise, then no amount of 'rational' talk is going to make him believe that the two occurrences have no connection. He has seen it with his own eyes—and he 'sticks to facts'. One way and another, there is no easy escape from a belief in magic: it is almost a closed circle.

'Briefings' then, efficient and factual, were not likely to have occurred in the painted caves. Obviously something did though: even if one is a paleolithic savage one doesn't penetrate into the deepest fastnesses of a cold, dark and uninhabited cave merely for the fun of tossing off a painting or two. Everyone who has seen these pictures has testified to their effect of intensity and deep earnestness and to the feeling when viewing them of being in a sanctuary. And what else than magic, now that we know something of its appeal for the primitive mind and the thoughts that lie behind it, could have been the purpose of these paintings of the beasts to be hunted? Mimicry is half the battle. Enact the hunt beforehand with success, and success will follow. Represent a creature, and behold, that *is* the creature—'something,' to quote from the successful field anthropologist G. von Koenigswald,[2] from whom we shall be quoting again later, 'something more efficacious than his desires, more real than his thoughts'. Represent it as pregnant and fecund, and the fecundity of the herds on which you depend is assured; pierce the beast on your walls with darts, contemplate the beast pierced with darts—or caught in a trap or falling headlong over a cliff— and, like producing like, your skill will be increased, your luck held, your hunt successful, your livelihood—meat for eating, fat for burning, skin for clothing, sinew for sewing—will be assured. Even indeed multiply your images on the walls, painting one on top of another, and you multiply your quarry. Perhaps in a way it *was* a matter of briefing, certainly it was all done for a practical purpose; but it was done in a highly emotional and what we should call a highly *im*practical manner.

Some of the remaining Australian Stone Age men paint their caves, and incidentally themselves, with designs that have ritual significance; and recently a film has been secured of a cave actually being painted. The head of the tribe is doing it, with an audience, or rather a chorus; and it is not an artist working so much as a sorcerer officiating, with his every gesture emphasized by ritual, song and dance. Now these Australian aborigines are an 'end product' and we must be careful with our comparisons. If however the paleolithic artists were not already priests or sorcerers, certainly they were people important enough to be fed and supported by the tribe in their 'specialized' job.

As for the ceremonies that took place, either at the time of painting or afterwards, we can only use our imagination—duly

The fantastic beast of Lascaux

restrained. Undoubtedly man loves dressing up, or to put it, justifiably, on a higher plane, he derives a great feeling of power and beneficence in mimicry. Most assuredly dancing—exciting and meaningful and rhythmical movement of the body—must have been practised extensively from the very beginning of the time that man came to be man. Undoubtedly any ceremony in the light of primitive lamps, the great painted animals seeming to move as the flames flickered, must have been tremendously impressive. Nevertheless, there is an inevitable temptation to respond romantically to every phenomenon found and to attribute to it something un-ordinary. That 'fantastic animal' for instance of the quoted description of Lascaux: just conceivably it is a poor or ridiculous imitation of one of the big bulls in the same chamber; it also looks irresistibly like a pantomime animal with two people inside it. If one man impersonated an animal, why not two?

And what about the representations of masked and animal-imitating men? One, masked and tailed and antlered, has been christened 'The Sorcerer'. But there is a difficulty here. If he danced in the cave, why depict him in the cave; if one draws in order to gain power over the thing drawn, why draw him? Perhaps paintings sometimes were commemorative—here was depicted, in honour, the greatest sorcerer of all time. Perhaps some of the masked men, so infrequently shown, were no more than hunting-decoys, depicted in their successful tricking of the animals.

Certainly the scarcity of pictures of human beings is significant,

'The Sorcerer' from the cave
of Les Trois Frères

as is also the fact that, so differently from the animals, they are usually shown formalized and highly unrealistic. This does support the magic explanation; for if delineation gives power over the thing delineated then man might well fight shy of portraying himself. This fear does exist among simple people, testified innumerable times: dismissed native servants piercing the eyes of photographs of their employers as revenge before leaving; refusing utterly to be photographed themselves. And presumably the more realistic the representation the greater the potential power of magic—and *vice versa*.

However, there must have been times when man wanted to picture man: to commemorate perhaps, or to strengthen the spirit and will of the tribe by remembrance of a great chief. There is for instance the strange 'hunting scene' at Lascaux. A gored bison, transfixed with a spear and with his entrails hanging out, appears to be charging a man lying prone before him. Beside the man lies his spear thrower and an emblematic bird on a pole. Retreating on the left—but it may have nothing to do with it—is a rhinoceros. The man appears to be bird-headed.

Here is most fertile ground for the exercise of the imagination. We will give the interpretation of that anthropologist from whom we have already quoted, von Koenigswald, from his book *Meeting Prehistoric Man*.[2] He points out that men have always been fond

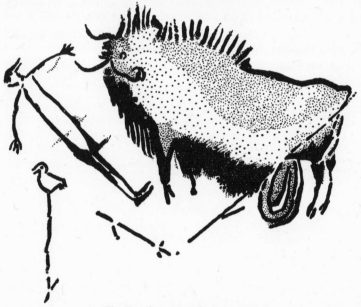

The 'hunting scene' from Lascaux

of symbolizing the human soul as a bird, for the soul can most certainly take wing from the body. Perhaps then there is here represented the soul of the hunter about to die. Perhaps even the bird is shown tied to the pole so that the hunter will *not* die. . . .

We are back with magic. We are even perhaps looking at the first glimmerings of religion, prayer rather than coercion. That is as it may be. At the least the paleolithic cave paintings show much more than that early man was artistic. He was *imaginative*—and, in his struggle to succeed, to control his environment, to be a man, his imagination was leading him up some strange paths. Sympathetic magic was not the only one.

12

Thou Shalt Not!

MAN had to become a social animal or perish in the attempt. As a Primate the life of the neuter herd was barred to him. As a carnivore and an ambitious one, seeking to kill large game, he would find the lone family life uneconomical and inadequate. Life as on a baboon hill was to him unthinkable—for the sufficient reason that he could think.

Now, when an ant community needs soldiers it creates soldiers, not merely a separate social cast but a separate physical form, with a mouth so much a weapon that the creature cannot feed itself. If, becoming economic, the ants need to store their collected honeydew, some of their number become honey-pots and obligingly hang themselves from the rafters. So that sex should not worry the bee, nurses are created with all the instincts to nurse but none to wed— 'mother to thousands but nobody's wife'—and males have the urge to laziness, lit only once by desire and then a desire so keen and selfless that the penalty of death in consummation does not deter them. The 'social' insects in fact live in a society that is virtually mindless and to all intents and purposes automatic. That is something for which man, whenever he is tired or discouraged, finds himself craving but which in his heart he knows he craves for in vain. His is the hard way and he has been given a brain wherewith to follow it.

One might think perhaps that Evolution would have worked more efficiently: if brain was to be the new implement of progress, why was not man equipped with one that did not bewilder and betray him into so many foolish and even self-destructive practices? But on second thoughts we must acknowledge that we can see no sign of Stone Age Man, in his struggle to become established, being ever in danger of extinction. We must beware then of thinking too easily that man's early practices were foolish, however strange and incomprehensible they may seem to us. They worked; with pain and grief no doubt, with very rough justice at times, but they worked. Sometimes the success was like that of the escapist at the street corner who has himself tied in chains: he sets himself free, but need he have got like that in the first place? At other times primitive man invented rites and customs that in truth we might do well to emulate.

Before the end of the Early Stone Age man must undoubtedly have reached the stage when he lived in a community of greater size than the family. The killing of such great beasts as the mammoth, such skilful steering to disaster of herds of swift-moving horses as is indicated by the bone-pile of Solutré—it is at the bottom of a cliff—presuppose a tribal organization. At Meiendorf (not far from Hamburg) there is a sign of the reindeer hunters making a communal sacrifice—we shall return to the implications of that—and on the River Don have been found remains of crude stone huts, with hearths therein, that were the work of Stone Age hunters who had not yet invented the bow-and-arrow, or pottery, or agriculture.* The cave paintings do not exactly necessitate a tribal way of living, but the assumption of it on our part is highly reasonable: the sons of even the most prolific mother could hardly have produced the sixteen-foot bulls of Lascaux and kept the family in food at the same time.

Now what did it mean to man to live in a community? For that matter what did it mean to him to live in a family? As a start we may be assured that it meant a great deal more to him than to any animal.

We need to look into this matter carefully. We have considered man's ways of thought in evolving the tool of speech for himself, and how speech was an inevitable necessity if social progress was to be made; we have watched man become the mighty hunter, and tried to understand his preoccupation with the magic control of the beasts he hunted. Now we must try to understand how he sought to control not only external nature but his own internal self. To live in a community meant for man, in one short phrase, to live *within*

* The bow-and-arrow seems to be an African Upper Paleolithic invention that only reached Europe in Mesolithic or Neolithic times.

a tradition. It meant living within a set of emotions and beliefs and rules. It meant being a member of a particular *culture.*

That is another word to approach with caution. The archaeologist has, it is fair to say, spoilt it for us by appropriating to it his own particular technical meaning. To him a culture is largely the 'artifacts', the things made, that the people of a certain time and place have left behind for his finding. This does not mean that the archaeologist ignores the wider implications; it means only that the material things are all that he has to work upon and that these therefore help him to define the culture he is examining. The word should mean on the contrary all that is immaterial and spiritual, all the intangible things to which the poor few remains of the tangible are our only guide. A culture is all that metaphorically has been 'cultivated' by the ways of life of the people to whom it applies. It will vary from all other cultures as the way of life varies; and the way of life will vary, fundamentally, with the environment of the people living in it. The Neanderthaler facing the last Ice Age had a different set of tools from the hand-axe users of Africa, because he lived in different conditions; his culture was different—in so far, that is, as the Pithecanthropine can be said to have had a culture. The men of Solutré had it seems very little art; from the Aurignacians they were, we should guess, a very different people with a very different tradition.

We need, I think, before we get down to detail and leave these concepts of 'tradition' and 'culture', to think of them in evolutionary terms.

One thing is of paramount importance, and that is to realize that when man becomes fully man the course of evolution assumes an absolutely new course. There are those who would say that with the full emergence of man the term evolution should cease to be used, that human history is not evolution; but I do not believe that that is a fruitful way of looking at things. What should be obvious is that it is pointless to talk of man in physically applied Darwinian terms, of the inevitable survival of the brutally fittest and so forth. If we manage to destroy ourselves as a race, then the supremacy of mind will have been wiped from the earth and no doubt nature will have need to start again—and whether mind would be made pre-eminent once more would seem doubtful. But while the human mind is pre-eminent then mind controls evolution; not only of the lower orders of life but of its owner as well.

And it will be, in the simplest terms, human traditions that will guide and control human development: not the inheritance of physical genes, which must take a second place, but the inheritance of what has been handed down by the mind, of 'know-how', and customs, and beliefs. Each 'culture' will have its own customs and beliefs; and when these meet and clash, as they will, it is there that the struggle lies and not as before between species and species. Sir Julian Huxley has expressed this idea very clearly in his book *Evolution in Action*,[21] when he divides the course of the cosmic story into three parts, Inorganic Evolution, Organic Evolution, and Psycho-Social Evolution—into which last we are now immersed. It is perhaps a difficult-sounding definition but nevertheless a helpful one. Genetic advance, he says, has given place to one by 'cultural transmission'. He makes a further fruitful suggestion. Perhaps with man, struggle for survival has changed to struggle for fulfilment—not for mere existence but for a fuller existence, not only for life but for a wider and deeper life. That must surely apply, by all the signs, to all men back to the very earliest.

Very well then: man evolving, man controlling himself, man struggling to become a social animal.

He has been called the only animal that by his own volition *abstains*. I doubt if he is the only one: Karl Lorenz has for instance pointed out that in dogs and wolves the weaker male will on occasion submit to the stronger by offering him his most vulnerable part, his neck, and that the stronger, though he may snarl and intensely want to bite, is somehow always inhibited. The point is that man goes very much further. The mammal's abstentions, for instance on the baboon hill, are made in the face of superior force and as a matter of common prudence, or, as in the example just quoted, implanted by Nature, which is chary of making a species self-destructive. But man: man has that 'picture' which William Golding, I think rightly, credited the Neanderthaler with power to produce; he has the power to appraise in the mind's eye the probable consequences of his action. An animal is gentle to its offspring, fierce to its enemy; it obeys merely the instincts of self-preservation and preservation of the race. But it does not think about these things; it cannot be said to be consciously either 'cruel' or 'kind'.

Such qualities are the prerogative of man. He is so vividly conscious of himself and, though perhaps not quite so vividly, conscious of the other fellow. He not only knows good and evil but is himself good or evil and knows that too. Man with his mind could not possibly have grown up without developing a conscience and the beginnings of a morality, a sense of responsibility and a sense of sin. And having done so he puts it all into words; and says:

THOU SHALT NOT!

There arrives in fact the *taboo*, a word we took over from the Melanesians presumably because it so impressed us. It entails much more than mere prohibition; it is not Law but Custom—and that is really the first useful point to make about it, that primitive man, emotional rather than logical, does not need to back his sanctions by lists of punishments since there is only one punishment and it is known and never needs to be mentioned: misfortune, the negation of life, *the bad luck of the tribe*.

The second thing to note is that taboo is often bound up with magic, indeed in many aspects it is magic, negative magic. A person may be himself taboo, in a way that is allied to being sacred—that aspect we shall come to later. On a lower level taboo is bound up most practically with bad luck, and in ways with which we can surely sympathize, since we observe them in our less logical moments ourselves. 'If I don't tread on any cracks in the pavement right up to *there* it will be all right!' How, since he can envisage the future, should man be anything but obsessed with the idea of good and bad luck?

Let us cover that aspect before we go on to taboos that will help man essentially to live as a social animal. If cave man practised positive magic by his paintings there is not much likelihood that he failed to practise negative or preventive magic too. Indeed we may imagine the preparations for a paleolithic hunting expedition as a most solemn and elaborate affair. Just as the hunter eats to gain magically the characteristics of the creature eaten, so he will abstain from eating all timid and skulking creatures, as the Madagascan soldier once abstained from hedgehog.* For a while before the expedition the hunter may well remain continent, regarding his wife

---

* Also, so Frazer reports, from kidney, which in his language has the same meaning as *shot*, thus bringing language into the magic orbit, a kind of literally painful punning. Cave man could have done the same.

as taboo, keeping within himself his virtue and strength. Then when the hunter has departed the onus will shift at least partly on to the wife and family. It would be tragic if, by their actions, and by the sympathetic influence of their actions, they should spoil the luck of the hunter when he by his skill and courage, no less than by his own observance of the magic rules of conduct, is doing his very best. The children must be brave and good, even perhaps receiving with due fortitude chastisement specially administered to prove how brave they are. More practically they will perhaps refrain from killing any *male* animal while the hunter is away, lest he too be killed; they will use no stabbing tools perhaps such as awls or needles, lest father and husband be gored; they will be careful with grease or fat on their hands lest across the magical ether someone else should suddenly find himself as it were a butter-fingers. In particular the wife will remain chaste and indulge in no promiscuity while the husband is away.

That last seems to have been a universal belief among primitive hunters, that a moral lapse on the part of the wife left behind will spell disaster to the hunt, so much so that the idea has on occasion worked backwards and disaster has sent the hunters hurrying home to wreak vengeance on innocent wives. There is here, as with other hunting taboos, undoubtedly a main element of practical magic; but there is surely something more to it, the bad luck being caused not by something materially akin, such as a greasy finger or an inadvertent scratch from a domestic needle, but by a moral lapse—sin will bring its evil consequences; the wages of sin are death.

On that idea we can legitimately swing across to the social taboos, those that govern more directly the ways of life of the tribe. For they centre round the ideas of sin and morality, ideas that a thinking, considering, imagining and wilful animal such as man could not help but acquire and acquire early in his history. We will take as typical the taboo against incest, and see where it leads us. It is the universal taboo, the strongest taboo, of primitive peoples.

And rightly so you may say. But consider a moment. Should not murder be considered a greater crime, or at least would it not have been so considered by early man, for did he not set much store by fertility and it is only murder that destroys a life? And

132

again, we are not shocked at incest among animals and even consider it natural or at times expedient among those we have domesti-
cated; and primitive man is much nearer the animal.

I think anyone can see that those arguments, particularly the last,
are specious. For the great truth is that man was struggling *out of*
animalhood—and at times acted as if he were more than dimly
aware of the fact. His job was, in terms of an earlier chapter, to
climb down from the electrically charged heights, the sexually
charged heights, of the baboon hill. He did it by inventing and
becoming conscious of the term *incest*, by widening the term greatly,
and by elaborating customs and taboos and myths so as to make
the crime not only difficult but so utterly shocking that no one less
than the hardiest criminal or the most virulent and insensitive
rebel would dream of committing it.

First, the wide extension of the concept. Most primitive tribes
are further sub-divided, into clans, moieties, phratries—various
names are given but clan is as good as any: a super-family living,
more or less, apart and as an entity. The almost invariable rule is
that one marries *outside* one's clan—we come to the well-known
word, which describes of course by derivation just that fact, *exogamy*.
Intercourse is taboo not only between parents and children and
between brothers and sisters, but between cousin and cousin, uncle
and niece, aunt and nephew, and not excluding adopted children.
Primitive peoples are always supremely conscious of relationships,
with separate titles for a maternal and a paternal uncle or aunt or
cousin, and a special single word for all one's relations that are
taboo.

Secondly the elaboration of the taboo. At the least it becomes
a damnable inconvenience, at the worst a mental torture. Such
books as Malinowski's *The Sexual Life of Savages*,[22] describing in
most loving detail the life of the Trobrianders in the South-West
Pacific, or Margaret Mead's *Growing Up in New Guinea*[23] or *Coming*
of Age in Samoa,[24] all testify to this. They testify too to the shock
administered to children (who otherwise tend to lead a most carefree
and untrammelled existence) when they are first brought up against
these taboos. If, says Margaret Mead,[23] a young girl goes to visit a
friend, at any moment the cry 'Here comes a taboo relative of
yours' will send her 'scurrying from the house, conversation interrupted and beadwork forgotten'. For on no account must the girl

133

be seen by her relation. As for brother and sister, who have up to now, no more than the age of seven or eight perhaps, been on the most innocent and intimate of terms, the change is drastic indeed. Brother and sister must no longer live in the same house, no longer sit near to each other, even touch each other; when they are together their conversation must be formal and circumspect and nice, as must that of any who are with them. The very concept of sexual love and brother-and-sister relationship must not it seems ever connect. With the Trobrianders as Malinowski knew them a brother must never witness his sister's act of love-making. If by chance he did so witness it, and there was no way of hiding the fact, then stark tragedy must ensue: all three involved will commit suicide.

This idea of the inevitability of tragedy if incest occurs, and that nothing, not even mere bad chance, can condone the deed, appears also in the stories and myths that men have built up around the subject. The Trobrianders have a story of a love potion. The boy makes it and leaves it where by chance his sister spills it over herself, to be overcome at once by its magic charm. Unable to withstand the maddening sting of passion she finds and chases her brother. They lie down together, and later make for a romantic grotto by the seashore and then lie together again and again. But all the while they are consumed by shame, and do not eat; and die. There finally they are found, with the plant that furnishes the love potion growing up through their breasts. The story, as Leslie Paul who quotes it (from Malinowski) points out,* is full of pity and compassion for the tragedy, but it does not attempt in any way to minimize it.

The story of Oedipus the King, a most ancient myth which Sophocles as was the custom of the Greek playwrights revived, is equally a tragedy of inevitability. Oedipus is cursed—and there is no way out of it. Taken at birth from his parents, he kills his father in a brawl without knowing the victim's identity—a murder about which nobody seems to mind in the least. But much worse is to follow. The town of Thebes is suffering from the plague. What is causing it?—someone must have sinned. Again it is Oedipus, whose queen is discovered to be none other than his mother. At last, convinced of the horrid truth (by the suicide of his mother-wife), Oedipus takes action that is at once prompt and terrible. He stabs

---

* In *Nature into History*,[16] to which book this chapter, as will be apparent, owes much.

the sight from his eyes, so that at the least he may never see again his beloved daughters whose lives he has blighted irremediably: the sins of the fathers shall be visited upon the children. Then he takes himself into exile, a blinded and pathetic and ruined man.

Now what does all this amount to, what conclusions can we draw from these customs, myths and taboos? Freud in a famous book *Totem and Tabu*[25] has built up an enormous hypothetical edifice on the Oedipus legend—on the idea, that is to say, that man has always harboured a desire for his mother and a consequential hatred for the rival who is his father. Freud creates, as it were, another myth or generalized story, wherein he imagines early man living in a 'primaeval horde' with the old-man-of-the-tribe in command. Some of the sons—the 'bachelors' of the baboon hill as it were—conspire to kill their father, succeed in their plan, and appropriate his wives. For ever thereafter man lives with a sense of guilt and the stain of murder upon him, and creates the incest taboo by way of expiation.

That may be so. But I think that anyone reading the book in question will end by feeling that Freud very much has it all his own way and builds fantastically on a very slender foundation. Opportunity for incest and great temptation to it there must undoubtedly have been; revulsion against it is equally inevitable as soon as man became the thinking, imagining, sensitive being that he is. But that it was only an instinctive, unconscious, unreasoning reaction and that incest was condemned not for itself but rather because it had led to the murder of the father, seems much less likely. Leslie Paul in his book already quoted puts forward a different explanation and I think a much better one.

Man, he says, can think forwards and backwards; he has in fact that new mental command over time which we noticed in the chapter on language. The parent will remember his own difficulties when he reached the age of puberty and he will know that his children have the same difficulties to face. Of course man may have thought this out a good deal less rationally and more emotionally than it is here laid down. But he *was* capable of 'putting himself in someone else's place'; and this he must surely have done. Here, says Leslie Paul, was being exercised exactly that 'act of identification' with somebody or something outside the self that the men of Lascaux and Altamira exercised when they thought of the hunt and painted

135

their animals, 'If a hunter, turned cave-artist, can enter into the life of a beast with such power that it breathes pantingly again after perhaps thirty thousand years, are we to suppose that his power to reconstruct the lives of his fellow tribesmen in his own mind is any the less?'

Man, seeing the temptation, saw also the difference between love and lust, the difference between sexual desire on the one hand and on the other family love, in particular that long-lasting dependence—longer lasting than with any animal—of the child upon its mother. If that love—a prolonged and constant and conscious thing, not the instinctive reaction of the animal—were to be allowed to change suddenly at puberty to a sexual relationship, what chance was there for the family to remain whole and healthy; what chance, with that example before them, would the children have of not falling into the same terrible and squalid error amongst themselves? Incest is the poisoned spear thrust into the side of family life that will destroy it inevitably.

And *that* is why it is a worse crime than murder. For it destroys not a single life but the life of the family, the clan, the tribe. It will drag it back, quite simply, to the animal level, from which it had escaped. . . .

That I think is sound reasoning. If it is, then Paleolithic Man is likely not only to have begun to practise the taboos and observe the customs that have been brought into existence the world over as a guard against incest but must also in the process have helped himself to develop a conscience and an awareness of the effect of his conduct upon others. And that is very much the same thing as saying that he became aware of morality and of sin.

We have then a picture of our paleolithic hunter, our cave man, our late Ice Age Man, not quite so simple or so idyllic (albeit very roughly and toughly idyllic) as we had first imagined. For undoubtedly all taboos against incest are harsh taboos and drastic. They seem often, as well they might be, the invention of people emotionally shocked and afraid; they go farther than they need go, because at any expense they must be effective. Nor would they often be disobeyed. Punishment in the form of the inevitable sickness and death of the criminal would be accepted and expected—and primitive man when he believes that sickness and death are upon him sickens and dies. Not only that. It is an aspect of sympathetic magic to

136

believe that, just as you can affect nature by your 'good' actions, your mimetic rituals and charms, so you must unfortunately affect nature by your misdeeds; badness, the mental sickness, of the individual will cause badness and sickness in nature around him, storm and tempest and drought and murrain, in sympathy with the internal malaise.

That is why very important people in primitive societies have to be so very careful. But more of that later.

13

Paleolithic Practices

S
O FAR back as the end of Chapter 8 we left Paleolithic Man physically, to consider him mentally and spiritually: his conquest of the power of speech, his art, his believed belief in magic and of the necessity of taboo. We called him then a painted and painting savage; and that is true, for to the end of his long run through the course of time he will never be anything but a savage. He was a predator and a parasite, to put the ugliest construction on his activities; a great and mighty hunter, to put the best. He will continue so until his way of life is pushed aside by a new way, a new 'culture'. There will come then what has been rightly called a revolution, the Neolithic Revolution.

But we have not finished with the Old Stone Age or the mighty hunter yet. We may even be sorry when we have to leave him. For he is both a pathetic and an heroic figure: pathetic, because he must have been so bewildered in meeting inimical nature with his unpractised mind and because his end was tragic; heroic, because his way of life was dangerous and challenging as perhaps was no other way until the days of the Homeric Greeks and the Norsemen of the Sagas. There is yet to be told considerably more of what we believe to have been his ways of thought.

There are two difficulties here, which we must not try to hide.

The first is not really a very great one. It might be held that since the paleolithic culture, the hunting way of life, is to fade out and be supplanted there is little significance in it and little point in seeking to describe and analyse it. But to argue so would be to fail to realize that cultures are not self-enclosed things, not water-tight entities wholly particular to a people. They spread and leak, just as

138

the genes of heredity must have spread with exogamy and indeed just because of exogamy; while beyond the confines of the tribe there must have been exchange of ideas as there are signs of the beginnings of exchange of goods.* It is an eternal point of dispute among anthropologists as to how much cultures 'diffuse'; but it is a dispute about degree not about fact. In whatever way or however completely the paleolithic hunters faded out they did not do so without handing on to someone the flame, feeble though it may yet have been, of spiritual and material progress.

The second difficulty is greater. It is the need to decide how much of spiritual progress can be credited to prehistoric peoples and in particular what can be attributed to what peoples, in the present context to the late paleolithic peoples. Anthropologists, devoted, intelligent and skilful, have collected for us pictures of all those still living or recently dying cultures that are the equivalent of the original Stone Age savageries; while the archaeologists with equal skill and integrity analyse and describe their significant finds. The job of the prehistorian is to match the two. He knows that what the anthropologist shows him are end-products and that customs like everything else must accumulate and change; but he knows too how amazingly conservative is man and that similar environments and ways of life do produce similar traditions and beliefs. He knows that he must guard against giving every archaeological find its most romantic and exciting interpretation; but he knows too that to be frightened to give any interpretation will get him nowhere and is not for that matter a very fitting way of paying respect to his hunting forbears whose superabundant courage he has been at pains to salute. He may be on a tightrope; but it is of no use whatever trying to stand still on it. As to deciding how much exactly of what is common belief and custom among modern primitives can be credited to paleolithic hunters and not to their successors, we can only be guided by two things, our sense of the reasonable and probable, and the pointers left behind by the hunters themselves in the way of their bones, their works and their possessions. As a next step then we will give a bare list of the things left behind by the paleolithic hunters that can give us some grounds for crediting more to the paleolithic mind than the belief in sympathetic magic and the

* e.g. sea shells from the Mediterranean found in the caves of the Vézère valley—see *What Happened in History*[26] by the late Professor Gordon Childe.

observances of taboos against sexual excess and malpractice with which we have so far credited them.

First, evidence of burial. From the times of Neanderthal Man onwards skeletons are found not only washed down and preserved by silt or sealed in caves or as at Cro-Magnon with evidence of violence and murder but also with marks of intentional, indeed what we should call reverent, burial. At La Chapelle aux Saints in the Dordogne was found such a burial in a rock shelter that seemed to have been specially selected for the purpose; beside the corpse had been placed fine flint implements and a joint of meat. Often the burial is below the floor of the cave being lived in. There is a stone pillow; the skeleton lies drawn up in an attitude of sleep or rest. With the appearance of *Homo sapiens* there comes evidence of the use of red ochre at the burial. Sometimes there are necklaces or bracelets, of ivory or animal teeth or shells. At Ofnet in Bavaria was found a neatly packed cache of skulls, all facing the same way.

Traces of body decoration—belts and head-dresses as well as bracelets and necklaces—are found not only in burials. There is also probable evidence of the mutilation of the body: some of the hands outlined on cave walls have one or more fingers missing.

Next in this purely factual list of discoveries there come all the 'small' art of the paleolithic peoples, *art mobilier* the French archaeologists called it, art that one could carry about. Earlier, we passed this over to talk of the more obviously significant cave painting. Nevertheless, it is of the two the more widely spread, appearing from Siberia down to Africa. It may be an engraving with the burin on bone or ivory, or a carving in the same material; it may be modelling in clay or a paste of clay and powdered bone.

Finally an isolated item of heaven knows what exact significance: a life-sized model bear. This was found in the cave of Montespan in the Pyrenees. On the bear's forepaws rested a real bear's skull. It had presumably fallen.

Now for the interpretations and implications. In speaking in Chapter 12 of taboos we were covering only what may be called the negative aspect of man's efforts to become a successful social animal. There must have been a positive side.

Let us bring in once more, circumspectly, the evolutionary viewpoint. Man is trying to establish himself; he is struggling both for existence as an animal and, in Julian Huxley's phrase, for fulfilment as a man. If he were any other mammalian carnivore he would, to the best of his ability:

> hunt and eat;
> propagate;
> stay alive;
> live in amity;
> play.

He would, that is to say, do these things as a species, so that that species might survive and even increase, might successfully exploit its environment, and might extract some *joie de vivre* in the process. This would be done not consciously but because it is the nature of the beast to do so.

Translate that into conscious and self-conscious and purposive terms, and what do we get? I suggest something like this:

> hunt and eat (as before);
> have, and bring up a family;
> conquer nature and avoid disaster;
> foster the tribal consciousness;
> afford outlet for the emotions.

There is this shift of emphasis because of course man has a conceptual mind, that busy mind always remembering, dreaming, scheming, apprehending.

Man must have become at an early stage aware of death and of the inevitability of his own death. Animals have the instinct of fear and self-protection; they can seem to us very touching and pathetic about death. But that is largely because we are looking at them with our own eyes of awareness—remember what a baboon can do with a dead body. By contrast, man must have felt death keenly and thought about it endlessly. His emotional life was not so disarrayed by death as it is sometimes with birds so that the loss of the mate leads to a pining away; but it must have been disarrayed. As for thinking, the inevitable thought was surely of some life after death.

That was not necessarily pure wishful thinking: primitive beliefs seem more often pessimistic and resigned, nearer to the

Greek Hades than the Red Indian Happy Hunting Ground. Nor is perhaps a life after death the right term. Primitive man seems to have been intensely aware of his own spirituality, of his difference in this respect from the animals: that is the enheartening thing about him. But we must not credit him with too much. He was not thinking of immortality; he was watching the dead body that a little while ago, perhaps a few seconds ago, was full of vitality, and thinking that surely somewhere the animating spirit must still be hovering. At least for a while.

At least until he had done something about it—until perhaps the flesh had disintegrated and he had buried the bones, until he had burnt the body. At the worst until he had broken the limbs or disarticulated them; at the best until he had decently laid out the body and buried it with splendour and ceremony, with its regalia and with its possessions and to the accompaniment of such deep thoughts and wishes and prayers as the mourners were capable of entertaining. There is much evidence amongst modern primitives of this belief in the temporary presence of the spirit, a presence that can be ended. Going back at any rate as far as Neolithic times, the group burials at Jericho seem to illustrate this belief: most respectful and ceremonial burial; but, on the next arrival, the skeleton unceremoniously swept aside in a jumble of bones and dusty trinkets.

Now does all this come from fear or from kindliness? Pretty obviously from a mixture of both, and a large measure of both on all occasions. Man is shocked and bereaved, more particularly perhaps because it is a universal belief of primitive man that death, however inevitable, is never natural but the result of some occult evil. But he is also frightened. He is frightened because he dreams. He believes in spirituality—we must not build up too gloriously on that fact—because he believes in spirits, and he believes in spirits because he can visualize, 'in the mind's eye'. Much of man's waking thought may have been dreamlike; but when he did actually dream and the dead appeared to him in dreams, what else was he to believe but that somewhere their spirits still existed?

Perhaps man thought that the spirit of the departed existed only so long as it was remembered and dreamed about—in which case, the more important the man, the ancestor, the longer would his spirit live. Another belief—vague belief, as all this was vague and illogical, felt rather than thought—must have been that the spirit would, or could be made to, depart; the spirit once laid, it would yet continue to exist but would no longer disturb the living. It had gone on a journey—that is an inevitable idea—a journey to another world. And whether it is a matter of good riddance or fond farewell, or an ambivalent mixture of the two, the mourners will want to help the spirit on its way. It may be a dangerous journey on which it has embarked—as some Australian aborigines believe—and so you will give it its weapon for self-protection on its way; in any case it would probably like to have its lifetime's weapons. It will also need food.

A hunk of meat beside the corpse! But the primitive mind is not thinking ridiculously. It is thinking symbolically—it always tends to think symbolically, sometimes admittedly at the expense of cold reason. Symbolically then the spirit may be helped towards the achievement of an after life and a safe arrival at his journey's end. Red is the colour of blood, and the blood is the life. Red ochre is not very hard to come by, or if a journey is needed to fetch it, surely well worth while. For painted on the living body it will be likely to help by magic towards a fuller life, and painted or sprinkled on the corpse it may even more efficaciously ensure a new life after death.

Such is the possibility. At the least we can visualize some sort of burial scene both for the Neanderthalers and for their successors, and much struggling thought and stirring feeling behind it.

One thing we must not do, and that is to project our own feelings too facilely into the scene. If the idea of burial under as it were the fireplace or the sitting-room floor horrifies us, or limb-breaking and the subsequent shovelling away of the skeleton disgust us, we must not jump to the conclusion that primitive man was disgusted but forced himself to these practices, nor the opposite conclusion that he was irredeemably insensitive. Ruth Benedict has something to say on this.* Any culture, she insists, must be considered as an organic whole; and until we know it as a whole, until we are aware of its full 'emotional background', we cannot understand isolated phenomenon from it. In other and more homely words, it is wonderful what in fact you can get used to, what you can accept if it is in the tradition of your culture and your times to accept it—just as industrial Britain accepted children in the mines or Cortes and

* 'Configuration of Culture', from the anthology *Primitive Heritage*.[27]

Pizarro accepted rapacious cruelty plus proselytizing zeal amongst their followers. As we cannot possibly know to the full the cultures of early man, at least we must not sit in judgement.

We do not even know whether or not the Neanderthalers and their *Homo sapiens* successors indulged in an abandonment of grief. Ruth Benedict (in the same article) can again help to guide us. Whatever primitive cultures have in common, she says, they do tend to divide into two opposing kinds, which she calls the Apollonian type and the Dionysian—Bacchanalian might have been a more familiar but partly misleading term. A people of the second type 'values excess as escape to an order of existence beyond that of the five senses, and finds its expression in the creation . . . of painful and dangerous experiences, and in the cultivation of emotional and psychic excesses, in drunkenness, in dreams, and in trance'; it seizes, in order to make emotional capital out of them, the crises and striking phases of life: birth, adolescence, menstruation, death, the taking of life. A people of the second type on the other hand play down all this and base their life on the 'theme of sobriety and restraint in behaviour'. Ruth Benedict cites as the latter type the Pueblo Indians, surrounded nevertheless by tribes of the opposite tradition.

Not that that must be allowed to give the wrong impression. The Pueblos, as any primitive peoples, also have their rites, their ceremonies, their dances;* it is the fundamental attitude to them that is different.

Now which of those two attitudes are we going to ascribe to Stone Age Man? Probably the correct answer is that we are seeking to generalize too much and that we can ascribe both, at different times and to different peoples. The hunter one could well imagine as an austere and restrained sort of person. But on the other hand one would imagine restraint of the emotions not to be a quality to appear early in the human tradition. The real point is that man is wedded to rites and ceremonies; always wedded to them, whether at one end of the pole excessive, hysterical and masochistic, or at the other dignified and restrained. They afford an outlet for the emotions, which is one of the five necessities that we have listed at the start of this chapter for primitive man's successful living (and the psycho-

* Described for instance by Jacquetta Hawkes in *Journey Down a Rainbow*[28] by herself and J. B. Priestley.

logists would say, surely rightly, for modern man's living too).
By affording a *shared* outlet they help achieve another necessity,
that of fostering the tribal consciousness.

Let us now look at another clue left behind by the Stone Age
men, for it may well have had something to do with their funeral
rites. Some of the imprints of hands on the cave walls—at Gargas
in the Pyrenees for instance—show fingers missing.

Professor W. J. Sollas, in his classic *Ancient Hunters*,[29] enquired
into this particular example of bodily mutilation most thoroughly.
He found it to be widespread: the ancient and dying race of Bushmen
in Africa, the primitive Dravidians of Mysore, the North American

Fingers sacrificed or pretend-sacrificed? Hand silhouettes
from the cave of Gargas in the Pyrenees

Indians (as we shall have occasion to observe later). The reasons
given for the practice are various: a badge of tribe or caste, a be-
trothal rite and mark of chastity for young women, a celebration on
becoming a grandfather (but somebody else's finger!), a bribe to
the gods to grant a wish, a drastic and spectacular symbol of
grief at a funeral. That last is perhaps the most usual reason, and the
more important the corpse the larger the practice amongst the
relatives left behind, so much so that the young and prudent would
seem to have insisted upon only a tip being taken off, to leave more
for a future occasion. To give a true picture and not a facetious one
however, there is the record of a fight among relatives for the
privilege, and Indian women regretted the forced cessation of the
practice just as some of them are said to have regretted the ending
of *suttee*.

Professor Sollas next makes the point that the more widespread a practice the older is likely to be its origin. Then he seeks to refute the possible criticism that the ancient cave imprints were of hands with a finger or two doubled under, that in fact the imprinters were only pretending. With a helpful and enthusiastic student he made experiments, coming to the conclusion that it was very difficult to pretend. And then he makes the final point, a good one, that sacrificial rites have a tendency to become less drastic, with substitutes for realities, and that even if the ancient hunters were in fact perpetrating a hoax on the cave wall, why should they pretend to a badge they hadn't got except that the badge was worth having and had once been a real one?

If one kind of bodily mutilation seems to have been likely, why not others such as have been observed among primitive peoples: scars and the raising of patterned weals, the filing or the knocking out of teeth? They are at least a possibility. Let us widen the scope, and also lighten the atmosphere somewhat, and look at the whole business of bodily decoration of every sort. It is an inborn craving and satisfaction in which literally no people has failed to indulge. It gives intense pleasure, as grooming and preening—and the comparison is neither insulting nor insignificant—give pleasure to all mammals and birds. But with man it gives much more than mere sensual satisfaction: it can enhance the sense of personality, it can enhance the sense of belonging to the clan or tribe, it can give great satisfaction through symbolism and magic.

Ice Age Man clothed himself of necessity (or near necessity plus a reasonably alert eye for the main chance), and incidentally in the process probably saved himself the trouble of evolving a hair-covering all over again. Nevertheless he probably wore his fur cape with a swagger; and, since partial is more revealing than complete nakedness, he probably became aware of the shaming fact, as Adam and Eve are said to have done, and proceeded to cover up his private parts. Thus clothing has always possessed a triple purpose: protection against the cold and the rain and the wind (and what winds there must have been in the lands at the foot of the glaciers!); the demands of modesty; and the chance to draw attention, one's own as well as everybody else's, to one's personality by changing the look, even apparently the very shape, of the body. Nor—though we are not to imagine any Stone Age Diors—should we underrate the paleolithic people's skill, sensitivity and inventiveness. Fine needles presuppose fine sewing; and, as the modern Bushmen show, skins can be made remarkably supple so that fine sewing is a possibility, while the better flint tools are certainly capable of 'cutting out' as well as of mere cutting. In the Grimaldi caves in Northern Italy a skull was found so encrusted with perforated shells that it has been suggested these were sewn on to a

Spanish ladies

cap which the buried person was wearing. In Eastern Spain there are paintings of a quite different tradition from those we have so far noticed, where the men wear imposing fur hats and the women quite elaborate dresses down to their ankles. (More about these paintings later.)

All these things, dress and decoration, the painting and scarring of the body, always *meant* something: that is the great point for us to realize. The necklace of wolf's teeth (such as found on 'the Red Lady of Paviland' in Wales) may have symbolized imperishable constancy, as did the North Star to the romantic Indian whom we noticed. Equally it may have served by sympathetic magic to

147

enhance the prowess of her husband away at the hunt (that is if the skeleton were truly a lady's which it may not have been). The hunter himself no doubt wore something special, even if it were only a bar of paint, to show that he was a hunter; the priest-artist, if there were such, appeared as no other than the priest-artist when he officiated in the depth of the cave; the dancer certainly dressed to dance.

Indeed, the dancer *dressed up* to dance. Paleolithic Man, obviously from his cave paintings, dressed up as an animal. And when he did that he undoubtedly *was* the animal and felt he was the animal—even when the prime purpose was not the dance but the decoy. Early man was indeed quite capable of being practical and mystical at the same time, because he drew no distinction between the two states of mind. Thus to paint oneself with grease and red ochre is for the Australian native a protection against wind and rain and insects; but that does not mean that it is not a life-giving spiritual protection too. So also perhaps with the Aurignacians. . . .

Finally, and most importantly, bodily decoration and mutilation are the *tribal* distinction. The boy at puberty—it is the men who are the more important in these matters, the women might perhaps have said 'self-important'—the boy will as it were parade with his companions; and on parade he will be awarded with a badge of the tribe. And in all probability the badge will be one that he will wear for life, and its bestowal will administer to him a never-to-be-forgotten shock—more of initiation ceremonies later. The inflicting of scars and incisions, the knocking out of a tooth, circumcision, and a barbarous and even more painful operation called sub-incision: all of these have been practised by primitive peoples throughout the world, and something of them—either more or less, as their cultures were 'Dionysian' or 'Appolonian'—must be credited to our early hunters. The Old Testament Jews are of course the classical example of the use of the rite of circumcision; and the scorn with which they regarded the uncircumcized is symptomatic and highly revealing. There is always in this practice of body-badging the fostering of what we should call the team spirit, a protective insularity, a 'we'-consciousness. There is always this pressure 'not to disrupt the tribe'.

.   .   .   .   .

As an extension of this idea, body markings and tattooings and paintings are very often *totem* marks.

Now this is the first time we have spoken of the totem. One has either to write a book about it or very little: there is no middle course and it is obvious which we must take here. But if we comfort ourselves with the truth that no modern person really understands totemism nor is now ever likely to, and that in these circumstances some pretty wide generalizations will be justified, we shall get by and with luck learn all that we need to learn.

Professor Sollas' definition of a totem is 'some natural object or phenomenon with which a person or a group of persons is associated in close and mystic union'. He goes on to say that if you ask, for instance, an Australian aborigine of the Crow totem for an explanation you will be told by him that he *is* the crow; that he possesses the crow and the crow possesses him; the crow and he are the same flesh, the crow is his elder brother.

He might also tell you that the crow (or the witchetty grub, or the cloud, or the kangaroo, but usually an animal and an animal that is hunted for food) is his ancestor. He might, if you had his confidence, add that the crow, or what-not, had care of his life, or of his soul. If he spoke the modern idiom he might say that the totem was his soul-mate—and if he did he would mean it much more literally than you would.

That is of course the trouble: the practitioner will not be able to tell you the real truth, or will not want to, or both. An aspect which Sir James Frazer concentrates upon is that the totem-holder will *protect* the animal which is his totem and will refrain from eating it, and naturally so if some one animal of his totem-kind possesses his soul. But then there is the fact that the totem animal that is so carefully protected *is* on special and sacrificial occasions eaten.

We must fall back on the idea that primitive man is always to us a queer mixture of the practical and mystical. He surely knew innately that he was also one of the animals and yet more than any animal. The primitive hunter's life was bound up with the animals: we may remember that phrase, 'he killed, ate and drew', and we might add, 'and thought and felt'. Mystically then, the animal was to him his blood brother and his ancestor; practically, if every clan of a tribe took upon itself the responsibility of con- serving a particular kind of game then the hunting of the tribe as a whole would be the more successful and the less likely at any time to sink down into famine and disaster.

In any case the totem was a *particular* animal (or insect or plant or natural phenomenon). We come back to the idea of badging, of belonging to a *particular* group. We come back also to the protection of the community by exogamy; for girls and boys of the same totem never married—and if totem and clan did not always exactly tally (as has sometimes been discovered) then all we can say bewilderedly is, the more difficult for the people concerned!

Now totemism is paramountly a hunter's belief; and once again we must suppose that the origin of a very widespread practice is very old, in this case perhaps almost as old as hunting itself. Indeed there was a time when anthropologists sought to explain all the cave paintings in terms of totemism—we might certainly allow them the bear of Montespan with a real head, hardly at any rate an example of pure art for art's sake. At least we can say that the fostering of the fertility of one's living larder by the protection of totemism and by the magic of painting would be very much the face and obverse of the same coin. And if it led on the mystical side to an increase in the feeling of brotherhood, in the consciousness of a common ancestry and even the beginning of some kind of ancestor worship, so much the better for the health and continued entity of the paleolithic tribes. Those serried skulls at Ofnet are surely a sign of respect for ancestors, as indeed may be all burial; in this case, since all the skulls face the setting sun, it may show more, the dim beginnings of religion.

Do not let us however claim too much for the paleolithic hunter. Where magic ends and religion begins is hard to say; but at present we will stick to magic.

What man wanted above all, and did his best to procure, by magic, by taboos, and by more positive customs, was in one word *life*. He wanted more, and more abundant and satisfying, life; he wanted it for the animals that were his food, for himself, for his family, his clan, his tribe—that wide generalization covers all five of the 'necessities' that we listed at the beginning of this chapter.

It also brings us to the only one of the physical finds that we have not at all brought into the picture. This is the *art mobilier*, the etchings on bone and ivory, the little models. The obvious and indeed necessary thing to say about this is that it is often highly skilful, appealingly beautiful, strikingly realistic—in the etchings of the mammoth more realistic than we ever knew until an intact beast was found in Siberia. It is the art of a new and self-confident and thriving culture that has time and energy and desire to decorate its possessions

Engravings on tusk and antler: charging mammoth
and the stag that looked back

and things of everyday use, and it needs mostly no implications of magic to explain it. But it has one exception. Much of the modelling is of the human form, and when this is so there is a stylizing and exaggeration about it and the form is usually feminine. There is obviously a significance there—which must wait for a later chapter.

14

On the Brink of Change

I T IS certainly a very good wind that blows nobody any harm. The great paleolithic hunter is destined to suffer a decline and fall, and the cause of his trouble is not going to be a colder and harsher world but the reverse, the final retreat of the ice and all the climatic and geographic changes that were to go with it. Before beginning to describe this change it would be well to try to give a word picture of the men of the later Early Stone Age. This may sound ambitious; but the point is that at least it *can* be attempted: as yet, and for the last time, the world of man is virtually in one homogeneous state of culture.

Australopithecus, half-man, we can assume has died out long ago—perhaps, as Dr. Pei, who helped to discover him, has suggested, because he lived too soft, not facing change and opportunity. Pithecanthropus, age-long hand-axe user, has probably gone the same way, at best is a skulker in recesses of sub-tropic Asia and Africa, with as much hope of survival as has the Bushman and the Fuegian of today. The slouching, pent-browed 'extreme' Neanderthaler has specialized himself to death, while his forefather has perhaps been absorbed into the conquering race. *Homo sapiens* has in fact by now unquestionably inherited the earth. And he is doing one thing in it and one thing only: hunt. He is already of more than one race—more of this later—but he is of a single species. Finally for the proper appreciation of our picture, he has brought us at long last down from geological time, from having to think in hundreds of thousands of years at the least, to a historical time scale, or more accurately a prehistoric, where a single thousand years is countable and significant.

Let us take as our heyday of hunting *Homo sapiens* the times of the great cave paintings, now believed to have been around fifteen and twenty millenia ago.

First man's achievements. He had flints that could dig, gouge, cleave, scrape, chisel, pierce, cut, bore, shave (wood and bone rather than faces) and engrave. Of horn and wood and bone and ivory he had spears and lances and daggers and picks and shovels and needles and awls and barbed harpoons. These last were as beautifully made as the needles; used originally for land hunting, they were going to prove even more useful in the lakes and seas. He had, no doubt, resins for sticking and sinews for binding and hafting and netting; he had probably baskets though almost certainly not pottery. He had, and must have had for some time, dugouts and rafts and birch-bark canoes. Somewhere about now, and probably in Africa, he made his second great hunting invention, the bow-and-arrow, another 'machine' like the spear thrower, and a better one, for multiplying and suddenly releasing the strength of the human arm. He had some mastery of the animals but little if any control. He possessed as we know great artistic skill. He clothed himself finely with skins. He dispossessed the animals of their caves and he sheltered himself also in hide tents; he even built huts of a sort, half sunk into the ground for warmth, roofed with turf perhaps, and sometimes possessing stone walls.

He talked, he shouted, he recited, he let gorgeous and portentous but not always very meaningful words babble out of his mouth. He sang and danced. He hunted sometimes by moonlight and knew well the phases and habits of the moon. He made love by moonlight, and went adventurously out of his clan to do it, not marrying the girl next door. He divided the necessary labours of earning a living between himself and his women folk: he did the hunting and made the tools for hunting; the women did the rest. He took perhaps— judging by modern primitive tribes—more of a hand in bringing up the children than do most modern fathers and all male mammals, being one would guess 'spoiling' at first and then when the times of initiation came fierce and portentous.

That picture which turns up so often in one form or another, of the paleolithic hunter's life as a scene of domestic bliss at the cave's mouth is, I think, rather dangerously misleading. To begin with he by no means always lived in a cave. Then that figure returning triumphantly with the slain deer across his back: more likely it would have been a bleeding hunk of horse or bison, killed and dismembered on the spot; even more likely there would have been no hunter appearing at all, but only womenfolk watching and waiting or performing, to an awed and uncomprehending scatter of children perhaps, some agonized ritual to bring him back triumphant or at least alive.

Do not let us however debunk the picture too much. It is simply that life was never idyllic. There was joy all right and no doubt laughter—most primitive peoples have much laughter—but there was often tragedy, and a good deal more worry and care and repression than we like to think of when we envisage 'the noble savage'. Freud has ousted the romantic picture painted by Rousseau; the truth probably lies somewhere between. No doubt the ancient hunter was boastful as modern hunters are boastful; no doubt his habits were not always nice; no doubt he at times released his tabooed and controlled animal spirits and desires in orgies and corroborees as the Australian aborigines do. Yet I think the final picture can be one of nobility. However shot through with fear and uncertainty, there must have existed a great self-reliance; and as Freya Stark says, who ought to know—she is speaking of Arabs living near the biblical River Pharpar—'when life is so precarious and held by one's own virtue always, there is great dignity with it'.

But domesticity was not his forte, for he was seldom a static home-keeper. Even when he was a cave-dweller he was probably so only in the winter months. When the spring came and even the tundra melted and burst into greenness and flowers and its terrible bitter dust-laden winds abated, then he set out to lead a nomad's life, following the herds and waylaying them in strategic places. Then there would be perhaps those feasts and corroborees, and meetings of the clans that enlarged the spirit and the mind as well as filling the belly and relieving the body.

Nor does man show himself to be static if we take the wider view in space and time. This idea needs to be considered carefully so that we may lead ourselves to the second aspect of this general picture, which is man's distribution over the face of the earth. I suppose if we stood far enough back we should see over the centuries simply a rhythmic shift of the herds and of the hunters that followed them, back and forth, North and South. For though in considering *Homo sapiens* after he has come successfully on to the scene we are looking at only the last of the four Ice Ages yet the ice even within that age had its advances and recessions. The result was that in the more northerly zones the hunter over the centuries was having either to shift his ground or to change his typical quarry, from horse and bison for instance to reindeer or mammoth. Even further South he would be doing much the same thing, moving to follow his traditional quarry and at the same time to avoid the return of forest and swamp as a 'pluvial' climate followed a dry one. Towards the end of the period, as the ice slowly retreated for the last time, the mammoth and even the reindeer must have become no more than a memory to all but those stubborn few who followed them up into the arctic—perhaps they composed a saga about it: Tarara *bim*-de-ayay (past tense), the day our forefather killed the giant elephant.

As for Paleolithic Man's distribution over the land, it must have been, whatever else, sparse. Until you begin to grow and breed, that is to say control, your food supply, you cannot like Abraham's seed multiply and cover the earth. This may at least have meant that as yet warfare between tribes was very infrequent: the Stone Age hunter needed a great deal of room—but he had it. On the other hand hard times may have led to two bad habits of mankind, infanticide and cannibalism. Some primitive peoples have been known to kill off their firstborn, believing it to be the weakest and reconciling themselves pathetically with the belief that its spirit will return in the next child to be born. Cannibalism has been fairly widespread amongst savage tribes, though never indulged in lightly and usually for spiritual, that is to say magical, reasons rather than material. Writers and travellers, being human, have a tendency to believe what they want to believe, and they often seem to want to believe the worst: reports of cannibalism may not always be true—Darwin for instance seems to have been wrong about the Fuegians—and similarly so-called evidence of the same practice amongst the Stone Age peoples, skulls perforated to extract the brain and so forth, could possibly be otherwise interpreted. As for infanticide, there is no material trace of it. Both bad habits are only possibilities, in one case perhaps more than possibility.

Really the most definite thing that can be said about how Paleolithic Man covered the earth is that, with the outstanding exception of the Americas, he turns up everywhere where you might expect him, that is to say wherever climate and terrain gave him the animals he knew how to hunt. That in practice did not give him a very great area. Down and up to something like 50° latitude from the poles there would at most times be ice—that cuts off a lot of Europe and Asia but in the southern hemisphere only affects South America which is out of the picture in any case. Height as well as latitude produced glaciation of course, and there were large patches over the Alps and Urals and Himalayas and a smaller one over the Pyrenees; mountain glaciations in Australia and Tasmania too. Across the equator there probably ran a wide belt of forest. The rest of the world, where there is not high mountain, is man's: South Africa, a very wide belt all round the Mediterranean, the plains of India and of China, a larger and less sea-indented East

Tundra beasts hunted and driven by
man: mammoth and reindeer

Indies and—Australia? Yes, Australia was first inhabited by man, it is believed, somewhere about fifty thousand years ago—and by *Homo sapiens* incidentally and not as some have guessed, looking with not too favourable eyes at the aborigines, the Neanderthaler. The seas there were no doubt low enough to make 'island hopping' not too difficult, but almost certainly there was no land bridge: that is one reason why we assume paleolithic boats of some sort; and birch-bark canoes the aborigines possess now.

Now this is rather a different picture from that of an exclusively cave-inhabiting person residing exclusively in Western Europe— which is the picture given fifty years ago and one that is still all too easy to accept. It must be remembered that this distortion was caused by a pure historical accident, that there were found both easy discoveries and intelligent enthusiasts together. Asia may one day capture the archaeologist's limelight and Africa to a large extent already has. None the less, it is still right to fasten most of the gaze on Western and Northern Europe, and it may well always be so. For there Paleolithic Man certainly thrived, there too the environment was sufficiently hard and challenging. Perhaps always in or near the tropics history is not much made, for the reason that these men, like half-man, 'lived soft'.

Now we come to the great change that Paleolithic Man was to suffer. It was a case of either 'Go North, young man' or learn a new way of life! The ice was going North, the edge of the ice, the tundra, was going North, the steppes and grasslands were going North. In the place of the last would come either, as in the Sahara, desert, or, as in Europe, forest, first mostly pine then mostly oak. More land, becoming unfrozen, would be available to man, though the gain would be partly offset by a rise in the sea level. This would give relatively a greater extent of coastline; and many lakes would be left.

The result of all this for man may be described as an increased activity for both legs and brain. We should not forget the brain; and by that I do not mean only that man was forced into making new inventions. Endless argument there must have been: 'What do we do now?'; untold heart sickness from hope deferred: 'Perhaps *next* year the hunting will be better.' Sometimes no doubt there arrived battle and murder and sudden death as one migrating people impinged on another that had elected to hold their ground. But the archaeologist has learnt that a 'culture' or a 'flint industry' can change on a given site without a complete change in the people practising it, and the greater likelihood is a battle of conservatism versus self-confident innovation rather than of arrow versus spear or hatchet against hastily grabbed harpoon. Yet even the former can be agonizing. Geoffrey Bibby in his book *The Testimony of the Spade*[10] cites a good example of the sort of thing that must have happened:

'From the antler of a reindeer the hunter can make a harpoon head with which he can kill a reindeer. With it he can equally well kill a forest deer. But if he then makes a precisely similar harpoon from the red-deer antler, it will break before it penetrates the hide of the next quarry. While our hunter is learning that harpoons of red-deer antler must be broader and thicker than those of reindeer horn, and relearning the technique of casting the differently balanced weapon—his family is starving!'

It is hard when conservatism can lead to death, more particularly when in the whole way of your tribal life conservatism has always been regarded as an asset and not a liability.

That however is theorizing. Of this time of incipient and increasing change there has been discovered a great deal—and much of it quite lately—to help us give the physical picture as well as the psychological. We must now meet new terms and learn of new cultures. We finished Chapter 8 with Aurignacian, Solutrean and Magdalenian. Those are the classic, the famous, the outstandingly successful Upper Paleolithic cultures, the first and last the essentially artistic, the middle perhaps the more warlike and the more practical, with its superbly made flint spearheads. Now we come to the Capsian, the Tardenoisian, the Azilian.

We can in fact do a bit of telescoping here. The discoveries made at Fère on Tardenois in Northern France and at Mas d'Azil in the Pyrenees (both in the last quarter of the nineteenth century) are now held to be of virtually the same culture. We can therefore talk either of Tardenois-Azilian or simply Azilian: there is little doubt which we shall do here. Azilian and Capsian both do two things: show a new way of using flint and a new way of painting.

But first let us, very shortly, trace the shifting of the old cultures. What we believe to have happened is that as the ice retreated the more adventurous half of the population (or alternatively the more frightened half, frightened that is of the people who were coming from the South) trekked North while the more stubborn or conservative stayed where they were and unwillingly absorbed a new culture. In Europe at least that theory can now be borne out by discovered facts. The first stage is around Hamburg where at sites called Stellmoor and Meiendorf the German archaeologist Alfred Rust discovered a Magdalenian sort of culture and the remains of many reindeer. Here was a summer hunting camp beside a lake, and the hunters had thrown into it what they did not want, the bones after the time-honoured practice of extracting the marrow and the antlers after cutting off the best parts for tools. There was also a particularly significant find of which we shall speak later, and a seven-foot pole with a deer's head on the top which if it was not a totem pole was inexplicable. All that dates at about 15,000 B.C.

Then further North. Along the coast of Central Norway there was again picked up the trail. The reindeer were now swimming the fiords, as they still do; and man was following them, as he still does. This time there were discovered rock paintings certainly not rivalling but definitely resembling the cave paintings of France and

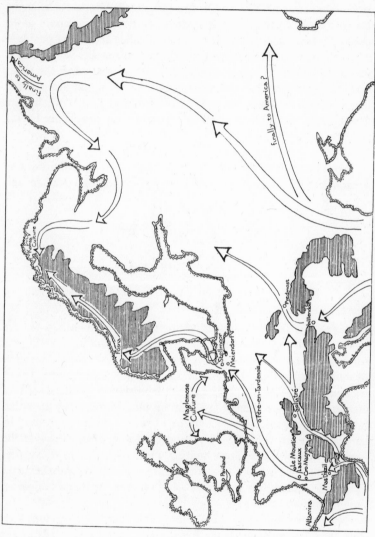

Over the centuries the hunters retreat North. Discovered sites and probable routes (only modern coastline shown). (*After Geoffrey Bibby.*)

Spain. In the cave of Pindal in the Asturias had been painted a mammoth showing a large red spot for its heart—it is accurate as to placing but incidentally—so Geoffrey Grigson[30] assures us, believing his own eyes rather than the textbooks—not very accurate as to shape. Here these later hunters—they are called the Fosna people— not only draw the heart but a line from it to the mouth: along it will travel, no doubt, the spirit of the life of the animal when the spear and the lance have been successful. So it is seen that sympathetic magic is not yet dead. What is also significant is that whales are drawn: in spite of following the old quarry these people are having to learn to hunt the new.

Now we come to the new cultures which are to grow in response to new conditions and sometimes to replace the old. Azilian and

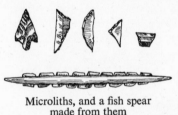

Microliths, and a fish spear
made from them

Capsian differ from each other completely in their paintings but are much alike in their new tools. These are largely an increase in gear for fishing but more interestingly the product of an entirely new way of manipulating flint. This is the manufacture of *microliths*. These, triangular, or in the shape of a chisel or miniature axe-head, or of a crescent moon, are usually less than an inch across. They are fitted into wood or bone, either singly or in rows; and they are used in particular as arrow heads. This is indeed the era of the arrow as the hunting weapon; it is forest hunting, more difficult and tricky perhaps than steppe hunting, sometimes as dangerous—you are hemmed in and the tusked boar is a terror—but on the other hand seldom so munificently rewarding.

Nobody knows where the Azilians came from, unless indeed they were the Magdalenians of the Pyrenees inventing a new culture on the spot. Their culture does also turn up further North, either found on the Danish coast, for instance at Maglemose (which means the Big Bog or Moss), or dredged up from the North Sea: at about

7000 B.C. these people were roaming these by now unfrozen flats—the only people ever to do so—and a couple of thousand years later they were hurrying away again to let the North Sea take their place.

The Capsian culture started at Gafsa in Tunisia (the change of consonants is irritatingly confusing and somebody's idea of Latinization) and its practisers, leaving no doubt increasingly desert conditions in Africa, seem to have penetrated into Spain, particularly Eastern Spain.

Here they executed their famous and highly distinctive, and already cursorily mentioned, rock paintings. The first thing to say about them is that they are very reminiscent of Bushmen rock paintings of a much later date, even down to the fact that the figures often show a marked tendency to steatopygy (scientific Greek for being fat buttocked), which tendency the Bushmen still

More figures from the rock
paintings of Eastern Spain

display. The other striking point is how utterly unlike they are to the masterpieces of Altamira and Lascaux. There is nothing loomingly solemn about these. They are cheerful and intimate and very lively; they depict scenes and in particular they depict people—people in head-dresses and sometimes quite elaborate clothes, and curiously elongated as if they were sunset-shadows of themselves.

Lastly the Azilian paintings—which are a most sad falling away. They are in fact no more than stripes and geometrical designs on smooth pebbles. Some show what might be considered significant likeness to numbers and letters, so much so that a serious proposal was once made that they were the paraphernalia of a sort of Stone Age school that taught the Three Rs. The Abbé Breuil and Professor Obermeier have patiently made a little sense out of them. By collecting all the stylized pictures of man made by early man—like the attenuated Capsian figures only more so—and by putting them in

161

sequences of increasing stylization, they do arrive quite often at something very like the Azilian pebbles. Even so however we are no nearer to understanding their use. Sollas' *Ancient Hunters*[29] throws perhaps a little light. The Tasmanians—now unfortunately all dead—had such stones, and once an old woman, arranging some, replied on being questioned that they represented absent friends, 'plenty long way off'. Had they something to do with ancestors—and once again had they something to do with magic?

What a pity that that old woman did not say more or that her descendants do not exist. But people do not carefully paint and

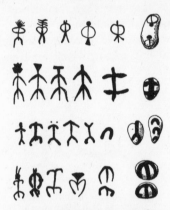

Professor Obermeier's comparison:
Azilian pebbles on the right

arrange stones for no purpose whatever. I think we can at least entertain two useful, if not startling, thoughts about them. One is to remind oneself once again of the strange and ever-present power of symbolism over man. The other is to wonder at the poverty of mind that he can sometimes show and incredible conservatism. Here were these Azilian people carefully painting signs on stones that had long ago lost any resemblance to what they were intended to portray.

Indeed that is very much the impression that we begin to get as the great hunters fade out: of poverty, physical poverty and sometimes of spiritual poverty. Perhaps what is called the Mesolithic Age might better be called a Dark Age, at the very least so far as Europe is concerned.

15

Poor, or Not So Poor?

THIS chapter carries the story, the material story, to the brink of what has been rightly called a revolution: the Neolithic Revolution. It means that we reach, in terms of time, to something like nine thousand years ago, round about 7000 B.C. (We are by no means yet in the era of certain dates but we can at least begin to think in less than millenia and use the term 'B.C.', merely subtracting a couple of thousand years from a dating in terms of 'ago'.)

The archaeologists have invented three terms to help them systematize and understand the times before man began to use metals and to be civilized. They are, as most of us knew as schoolboys even though we may have forgotten now: Paleolithic or Old Stone Age, Mesolithic or Middle, Neolithic or New. Mesolithic is the least useful of these three terms, and indeed it is perhaps rather a pity that it was ever invented. It tends to confuse, and it can even mislead. Authorities disagree as to what should be included in the Mesolithic—many would put the Azilian culture within it—and in some parts of the world, the Middle East in particular, no one can very well pretend that a Mesolithic Age existed at all.

The danger is this: one naturally assumes that the three are consecutive in history, first Old, then Middle, then New. Nothing could be further from the truth. The Paleolithic certainly comes first; it is universal and it lasts a very long time. But, to repeat, that is the last time that man's way of life can be counted homogeneous: from now on there is overlapping.

We shall do much better if while sticking to the terms—they are useful and accepted—we cease to think in terms of 'stone' and 'stone age' at all and look instead at what lies behind them. By and large, paleolithic is a way of life of steppe and tundra hunting, *open* hunting; mesolithic is a way of forest hunting plus fishing; and neolithic is a new way entirely—hence the phrase 'neolithic revolution'—when man became a farmer and a dairyman and a herdsman. *And the three continued to exist in the world side by side.*

The world is changing and all three are reactions to that change. The first, and we have dealt with it extensively, is the conservative reaction, of trying to carry on as much as possible in the old tradition. It remains in patches, in Australia for instance, but mostly and typically squeezed up on to or near the edge of the ice. The steppes of Russia and the tundra of Scandinavia and Siberia will still be open hunting country, though never so prolific as in the good old days; the mammoth will be exterminated; the people, hungry, will spread into Greenland and the Americas, and change in the process. The third reaction is of course the successful one; we will deal with it anon. The second, the mesolithic, is really an unsatisfactory compromise. You don't flee from the encroaching forest, you accept it and make the best of it without doing very much about it. You go on hunting but change your ways of hunting. Instead of living on auroch and bison and reindeer you live on the forest red deer, the wildfowl of the lake and mere, the fish of the river and sea and, in particular, on shell-fish.

That is the descent: from the hunt of the horse and the mammoth to the gathering of cockle and oyster.

There you have the spectacular view of the change. Let us try to be fair however, and take a closer and more considered view of the Mesolithic Age. Men were still hunting, and to fight such as the forest wild boar must have needed nearly as much courage as to face the trampling elephant or the stampeding herd of horse. It was rather that in this way of life men were not showing much intelligence or initiative. They were squeezed against the water's edge rather as their Northern brothers were squeezed against the ice, and they were not yet finding either of two successful ways out, build out over the water or clear the forest. Nevertheless the Mesolithic people have two claims to fame, having given posterity a couple of possessions for which it may be very thankful: one inanimate, the pot, one animate, the dog. They are indeed something of a paradox and deserve to be looked at more closely. They are typically European and their sites are discovered in Britain and in particular on the east coasts of Denmark. They are known as the Kitchen Midden people.

They are thus known because they lived, literally, on a slowly growing mound which was the refuse from their meals—animal and fish bones but predominantly millions and millions of discarded shells of oyster and cockle. It must have been a messy and smelly and also perhaps a muddy existence. There are signs of open hearths but none of any kind of huts; the climate however of these times was warm.

Whether it was a lazy existence or very hard it is difficult to tell. Perhaps it alternated between the two. When the hunting was unsuccessful then the women and children were set shell-fishing all the harder—the men would hardly demean themselves no doubt—and the diet became almost exclusively shell-fish.

Perhaps this monotony, or an occasional poisoning, forced on

Kitchen Midden pottery

the invention of the *container* in which food could be boiled. There may be mud about; but to choose the right mud, to mould it and get it to stay moulded, to fire it so that it completely changes its constituency—the first successful chemical experiment perhaps—and becomes hard and heatproof: all that, as anyone will know who has tried to be a potter, represents both hard thinking and hard work. It is a major invention. The pots of the Kitchen Midden people were large, rough and thick. They curved slightly to a point underneath, and must have rested on the embers supported by a ring of stone: the first cauldron, and the first rich smell of soup.

The most skilfully produced flint tool of these people is a thin regular knife blade which may reach twelve inches. They also have the microlithic arrow head—the miniature flint is often considered as the typical mesolithic tool—together with an axe, useful for wood-trimming but not good enough for serious tree-felling, that

165

was really a 'hand-axe', but a well-made one, fitted into an antler which was in turn fitted at right angles into a wooden handle.

Another interesting find, the find incidentally that led to these middens first being excavated, was a long four-toothed comb made of bone. The earliest discovered comb is not necessarily the earliest used; but matted, or perhaps mud-daubed and insect-proofed, hair is

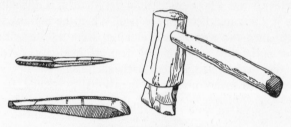

Mesolithic flint blades and axe

a distressing badge of savagery—it was one of the aspects of the Fuegians that revolted Darwin—and it is pleasant to think that sleek hair, or at least something approaching it, has come into the world. We must obviously not debit the Mesolithic peoples with too much poverty of spirit or lack of self-respect.

For instance, nobody with poverty of spirit would have domesti-

The bone comb from Meilgaard: 2½ in. long

cated the dog, and fear of sentimentality must not lead us to underestimate that achievement.

'Then the Woman picked up a roasted mutton bone and threw it to Wild Dog, and said, "Wild Thing out of the Wild Woods, taste and try." Wild Dog gnawed the bone, and it was more delicious than anything he had ever tasted, and he said, "O my Enemy and Wife of my Enemy, give me another."

The Woman said, "Wild Thing out of the Wild Woods, help my Man to hunt through the day and guard this Cave at night, and I will give you as many roast bones as you need. . . ."

Wild Dog crawled into the Cave and laid his head on the Woman's lap, and said, "O my Friend and Wife of my Friend, I will help your Man to hunt through the day, and at night I will guard your Cave. . . ."

When the man waked up he said, 'What is Wild Dog doing here?" And the Woman said, "His name is not Wild Dog any more, but the First Friend, because he will be our friend for always and always. Take him with you when you go hunting." '

That was no doubt the way of it. If we wish to supplement this —not substitute it—with a more scientific description than Kipling's[31] we can go to such a book as *Peasants and Potters*[32] wherein the Oxford archaeologists Harold Peake and H. J. Fleure speculate on the physical origin of the new acquisition and suggest a double one, the Dingo, a Husky-like creature, in the East, and a smaller beast, *Canis pontiatini*, in the West. The important thing is the happening. So far man has pitted his wits and courage against the rest of the animal kingdom, has hunted it and fought it, not without nobility and thought and respect on his part. Now for the first time he exercises his superiority directly over the mind of the animal. It is a *symbiosis*, on a relatively high plane. Each partner has forfeited something: man his freedom from responsibility for any creature but himself; dog, a large part of his wild nature. Both, and not only dog, will have their character altered by the partnership. More practically and obviously, man will have his fowling and his forest hunting helped immensely; even by the mere trusting and trustworthy presence of his friend he may have his fears of the outside and the dark and the unknown allayed.

The dog may well have been one factor that helped the Kitchen Midden men to be not only reasonably successful in their poor and marginal way of life—marginal in more ways than one—but also content in it. Another may have been that it was not a way likely to create enemies, a static and self-contained life. The fact remains that he did stay satisfied for a very long time. His culture thrived, it has been calculated, for something over two thousand years: at Meilgard in East Denmark the shell-mound was eight feet thick.

167

But there is something more than that. Other and better ways of life developed contemporaneously in the Middle East, and slowly spread to the rest of the world, Europe included; yet a conservative minority seem to have stuck doggedly to their old ways—'Poor Whites' Geoffrey Bibby[10] has called them—and at one site in Denmark they continued until what modern methods of dating give as 2200 B.C. Then, finally and before the old culture petered out, two things happen: the old take on some of the implements of the new, and the new take on some of the old.

The latter is surprising. What should successful and energetic farmers want from this remnant of fishing and hunting 'natives'? Perhaps they had the sense to realize that all experts have something to impart if one treats them patiently; perhaps at least they did what the Normans did with the Saxons in this country and no doubt the Romans with the Celts, took them on as serfs and servants. It would be at least poetic justice if the Kitchen Middener should have been taken on as scullion and kitchen maid.

So much for the typically mesolithic. We must remember that there were obviously no hard and fast lines of distinction. What we have described is simply a typically transitional way of living a hunting life between the times when the last Ice Age ended and when the farmer and herdsman and forest-clearer and megalith-builder swept westwards and gradually—very gradually apparently—persuaded the natives to change their ways. More or less this kind of hunting life was going on everywhere: fishing and sealing if near to the sea, more fowling if by the meres, more in the old way of open hunting where there was parkland, entirely the old way in a few remaining spots, though nowhere so happily prolific. Everywhere, by all the signs, it was a difficult and unrewarding time, a time when the human spirit was not exuberant, for there is little art. But, as I think we have seen, it was by no means a time of complete poverty, either of living or invention or ideas. The very fact that in these times the hunting clans must have been on the whole more self-contained and static may have fostered the growth of slowly strengthening (and slowly hardening) customs and traditions.

Next we shall try to assess the customs and traditions that are likely to have existed before the Neolithic Revolution. But before ending this chapter one form of wandering does need more than the passing mention that so far it has only received, that is man's entry into the so far empty Americas.

When it happened is still a matter of dispute. How, is pretty well agreed: via Siberia and Alaska and the Aleutians, either by island-hopping or by a land or ice bridge. The likelihood is that there was more than one wave of migration and that they took place between 10,000 and 7,000 B.C. Those who generation by generation made the slow journey were perhaps originally the Solutreans (Chapter 8), perhaps the Maglemosians (Chapter 14), perhaps both. Very much later the Eskimoes followed, but did not penetrate South. The earlier waves did of course penetrate, right down to the tip of South America; and that is something to wonder at: however long it took it is an amazing trek, from Europe, or at the least from Asia, up across the bridge of the North, down across the neck of the new continent and the equator, and finally right down to the cold inhospitality of Tierra del Fuego. These wanderers brought with them traceable skills in flint-making, in bison hunting, in rock etchings. One migration at least brought the dog; but the American Indians had never seen the horse until they were faced with the Conquistadores of the fifteenth century A.D.—when they believed them some strange single animal, centaur in fact, but soon learnt both their mistake and the riders' skill. Whether the Neolithic inventions, crop-raising and animal husbandry, came across the bridge too or were made all over again, no one has yet been able to say: it is an interesting point for the diffusionists and anti-diffusionists to argue.

Whatever was brought over in the way of belongings and techniques, one thing is certain, and revealing. They brought over religious customs and beliefs that in the new atmosphere took on sometimes an added harsh intensity and sometimes even an added cruelty and ferocity.

16

Old Ways of Thought

I N 1841 a Mr. George Catlin published in two volumes *Letters
and Notes on the Manners, Customs and Conditions of the North
American Indians, written during eight years' travel* [1832–39]
amongst the wildest tribes of Indians in North America.[33] He starts
Letter No. 22, 'Mandan Village, Upper Missouri':

> 'Oh "*horribile visu—et mirabile dictu!*" Thank God, it is over,
> that I have seen it, and am able to tell it to the world.'

This is not his usual style; he has been deeply and genuinely
moved. He continues:

> The *annual religious ceremony*, of four days, of which I have
> so often spoken, and which I have so long been wishing to see,
> has at last been enacted in this village; and I have, fortunately,
> been able to see and to understand it in most of its bearings,
> which was more than I had reason to expect; for no white man,
> in all probability, has ever been before admitted to the *Medicine
> Lodge* during these most remarkable and appalling scenes.

Now this is where we in this book must tread delicately. For we
are approaching religion; and the beginning of primitive man's
realization and practice of religion, the time of it and the manner of
it, are very much a point of dispute and always have been. There is
no agreement amongst the anthropologists.

I have introduced religion at this particular point in the story
after due thought. We have reached the stage where one way of life,
the hunter's, is waning and where another very different way, the
agriculturist's, the herdsman's, the farmer's, the peasant's, is dawn-

ing. When that new way is really established religion will receive a new orientation. We must therefore, before we reach that point in pre-history, consider what it was likely to have changed from. On the other hand religious rites and practices do presuppose some considerable leisure in which to evolve them and some considerable tribal organization to implement them. We have credited the later Paleolithic peoples with at least some tribal organization and there is good ground for doing so. But it may not have been very strong or very permanent. The change has now come however from the hunter of the wide parkland and steppe and tundra to the fisher-fowler-hunter of the forest and the swamp and the shore—*in*-fighting with nature one might say—and with the tribe rather more static and turned in upon itself, rites and ceremonies may have had more chance to grow.

What it really comes to is that we are being cautious and conservative. The customs and beliefs that are now to be reviewed must surely have arrived before the Neolithic Revolution became an established fact. *How* long before, it is hard to tell; and if the reader feels that in any or all instances they must have arrived earlier than is here suggested he is certainly entitled to his opinion. The important thing is to see, whenever exactly they may have arrived, what they were. We have already talked of Sympathetic Magic, and Exogamy and the Incest Taboo, and Totemism, and certain aspects of reverence for, or fear of, the dead. Those we can legitimately believe came early; they centred, it was suggested, about the paramount need to prevent the disruption of the communal life. Now we shall have a great deal more to tell, and the same compelling causes will be there. But these will expand into something wider and greater—if less easily definable. As before, we will tie ourselves where possible to the discipline of observing the evidence of things discovered, 'the testimony of the spade'. No spade however can turn up the dreams and the imaginations of man: our own imagination must therefore not be too closely clipped.

We return to Mr. Catlin and the Red Indian village of the 1830's. Those Indians were then living, it would be fair to say, in a culture more or less mesolithic. What we are going to describe centres round rites of initiation, the reason for this choice becoming clear, it is hoped, as we proceed.

171

The four-day ceremony begins not on a certain date but when the leaves of the willow trees by the river are judged to be fully out. It begins dramatically and suddenly with a great hullabaloo in the village and a great show of excitement and alarm. There is seen coming across the plain a man painted white and dressed in white. He is ceremoniously met, and he announces that he is 'Nu-mohk-muck-a-nah' the First and Only Man, who has survived a mythical flood. He proceeds to open up, and orders to be cleared and prepared, the mystery lodge or medicine hut wherein the initiation ceremonies are to be enacted. He spends most of the rest of the day being led to the huts of the village, where before the owner of each in turn he explains his mission and from each collects a hatchet or a knife, some sharp flint tool. These he deposits in the medicine hut, and departs, no one knows whither. At the end of all the ceremonies these flints are thrown into the river as an offering.

The next morning the First and Only Man reappears. He now leads into the medicine hut the young initiates who are to suffer the great ordeal. In this instance there are about fifty of them. They are naked and painted and carry their arms. They arrange themselves around the hut and the First and Only Man harangues them, encouraging them to trust in the Great Spirit for their protection in the ordeals that are before them. He then appoints a master of ceremonies, hands over his wand of office which is his medicine pipe, and makes his farewell: he is going back to the mountains in the West, whence he will assuredly return in a year's time to open the lodge again. He is leaving the initiates to remain in the hut for four days and nights, *without food, without drink, and without sleep*.

For the first three days, while the initiates and their master are left in the medicine hut to their prayer and fasting, a symbolic dance is being held outside before an audience of the whole tribe and at increasingly frequent intervals. Mr. Catlin describes this dance in detail, bestowing on it such confident and disengaged adjectives of the nineteenth-century amateur anthropologist as 'grotesque' and 'amusing'. It is a *Bull Dance* and the chief executants wear bisons' pelts and head-dress. There are bears and eagles and antelopes being impersonated, and much meticulous and serious miming; and the result is that the Great Spirit has been successfully importuned to ensure good hunting for another year—a result which is duly conveyed to the initiates for their encouragement. But the climax is not

172

yet; for the Evil Spirit, though challenged, has not put in an appearance, and until he does so and is shamed and conquered the initiation ceremonies cannot proceed.

On the fourth day the Evil Spirit arrives, mysteriously from across the plain like his predecessor. But this time not calmly and directly; rather, strangely, madly, in a zig-zag course. He is painted jet and shining black, with white fangs for teeth; the tribe howls and shudders. The fiend shrieks back too; he chases the women, who fall over each other in terror to get away.

But the master of ceremonies has come out of the medicine hut. There follows a battle of wills:

'Surely no two human beings ever presented a more striking group than these two individuals did for a few moments, with their eye-balls set in direct mutual hatred upon each other; both struggling for the supremacy, relying on the potency of their medicine or mystery. The one . . . frowning everlasting vengeance on the other, who sternly gazed him back with a look of exultation and contempt, as he held him in check, and disarmed under the charm of his sacred mystery-pipe.'

There is more realistic byplay, too lewd to be described, and finally the fiend, exhausted and with mud and indignities heaped upon him, withdraws amidst the laughter, the cheers and the delight of the crowd. Success has been achieved; everything is right; the grim initiation ceremonies can begin. Back in the medicine hut, with the Chief and his elders appraising and approving, they do so.

These are best told shortly and objectively.

The initiates, a few at a time, have wounds made in their flesh beneath the muscle and strong wooden splints inserted therein. There are two splints sticking through the muscles in each leg, two in each arm, and two underneath the muscles of the back or chest. To these last rawhide thongs are attached and by the thongs the initiates are hauled up and suspended from the roof. From the other splints may be hung the boy's arms or perhaps a buffalo's skull as extra weights—all this while they are expected to show, and do show, no sign by sound or expression of grief or pain.

Now torturers come, and spin the hanging boys on their thongs.

173

At last the initiates cry out, praying to the Great Spirit. The torture continues until they faint.

They are let down and the splints by which they have been suspended removed.

They are not helped. When they have recovered sufficiently, they crawl, with the other splints and weights still upon them, to another part of the hut where sits an Indian with a hatchet in his hand, and before him another buffalo skull. The initiates place their left hand upon the skull, and a finger joint is lopped off. It is a sacrifice. Some offer two fingers.

Their sufferings are not yet over. In groups of six or eight they are led outside. Here another frenzied dance is in progress. They

Initiation ceremony. The final dance or 'last race'—copied from one of Mr. Catlin's paintings

must join in. Lashed wrist-to-wrist to two fresh and strong young men, each has to run and stagger round. They fall and they are dragged. By the dragging the remaining splints with their weights and paraphernalia are pulled out from the flesh—only in this way may they be pulled, and the dragging goes on until all the splints are released.

Then and then only can the young man's relations take them and succour them.

Now those are the practices of a Red Indian tribe of a hundred or so years ago. They are not the practices of Stone Age men; and the American Indians had by the time the white men arrived notoriously slid into some of the cruellest forms of sadism and masochism that the world has ever seen.

But, as Mr. Catlin is at pains to point out, these Indians were a noble race and in almost all other ways admirable.* This description is not here inserted, obviously, merely to harrow the reader. It does show, it is held, the *sort* of thing that *may* have been done by the true Stone Age men after they had achieved a stable tribal society. It shows, one would imagine, an *exaggeration* of what may have been done; it has as it were a hectic flush, and that fact may in itself enable us the more readily to discern and appreciate the outline of its true and basic features. The initiation rites of the Aruntas of Australia, which have often been described, are not so terrible. The imitative dances performed for the benefit of the boys are less hysterical and more cheerful. But the circumcision and sub-incision to which they are subjected is ordeal and shock enough. There is in fact much in common in all these rites wherever they have been observed, and it is possible for us to get down to a sort of common denominator.

The young men at puberty are taken from their tribe, their family, their mothers; they are segregated. By act or ordeal they have to show their fitness to be considered of man's estate. They have demonstrated and expounded to them the rites and mysteries of their tribe and sex. In ways that are truly shocking, and meant to be shocking, they are at once given a tribal badge and accepted into tribal membership. That is just about the irreducible minimum of it all.

Initiation ceremonies, we can see, are one more practice that helps towards that paramount necessity, to weld together the clan, to keep its identity undisrupted and its moral health and self-respect intact. But we can now go further and deeper. In many aspects these initiation ceremonies are bound up with religion.

Frazer has defined religion as essentially 'the propitiation of personal beings regarded as superior to man'. Sir Edward Tylor, sometimes called the Father of Anthropology, talks of religion beginning in 'the belief in spiritual beings'. We might combine the two and widen them a little and speak of religion as 'a belief in spiritual beings superior to man, and the rites and observances that such belief calls forth'. Perhaps that is as near as we can get: what matters is that we must be wide and tolerant in our definition. What matters even more is to realize how religious all primitive peoples are and must always have been. You can either be a materially minded evolutionist

---

* Tragically, they were wiped out by smallpox soon after Mr. Catlin's visit.

in this matter and be startled by the fact; or be a spiritually minded one, holding that God chose an animal to be evolved into man in His own image, and so accept the fact as obviously inevitable. In either case the fact is there. We have said that 'Economic Man' certainly did not exist in the beginning, and by that we did not mean that man was not necessarily self-seeking nor lacked most wilfully held desires. We meant that those desires were seldom for purely personal or purely material rewards. The obverse side of the statement that early man was not an Economic Man is to say that he was a Religious Man.

He was, to put it a little less highly, and by every account that one can read, a man suffused with the idea of the supernatural. To make an easy, nevertheless justifiable, paradox, the supernatural was to him natural. Many have called the mind of primitive man 'pre-logical', completely unscientific, unable to appreciate natural cause and effect—the French philosopher Lévy-Bruhl[34] has led that school. But most anthropologists feel, I think, that that is going too far. Rather it is that the primitive mind prefers to think mystically and symbolically. Things are not just things, Nature is not just Nature; it would have been incredible if man, suddenly born to awareness of it by his great imaginative mind, could have thought of Nature so coldly and so unemotionally. Nature was overwhelming and wonderful and frightening. Everything in it had an *influence*.

Mana is the great word. It is originally Polynesian, but practically every primitive peoples have the idea—the Dakota Indians call it *ton*, the Iroquois *orenda*—and anthropologists have appropriated the word and given it a general meaning. If a thing has *mana* it has a mystical and unseen emanation, a *power*, good possibly and indeed probably, but more essentially to be respected and treated as dangerous. The gods have *mana*, indeed their *mana* can never be destroyed. But so has the woman who at the time of menstruation is taboo, so has the Indian's medicine pipe, so has the Australian's *bull roarer*, so indeed has anything in a significant circumstance or at a significant time. Nor need we feel superior about this. The bull roarer is with us a child's toy, streamers caught in the wind that revolve and make a noise. The Australian aborigine will spend a happy day trailing it over his crops to impart its beneficent influence. But so can we spend a happy time distributing a greyish powder which we are taught to call a fertilizer. Both we and they are taking

176

the results purely on trust, and the fact that we are more likely to be rewarded is our good fortune and not, so far as the actual practice goes, due to our superior intelligence.

But is *mana* religion? Or is it merely magic? The answer is of course: it depends how it is regarded. We must allow primitive peoples to have been as varied in their religiosity as we are ourselves. To the clotted Neanderthaler the hind had *mana* who as he watched her gave birth to her fawn; the stone that tripped him had *mana*, the suppurating wound even, merely because it suppurated; the dark sky that sent down the lightning, and the stream that gave him life-saving water and cascaded with spectacular force over its rocks and ledges. To the Indians of our Mandan village it is not the stream but the spirit of the stream (to which offering of the flints is made) that has *mana*; it is above all the Great Spirit that has *mana*, sufficient in fact (when duly encouraged by ritual) to defeat the power of the Evil Spirit. To the 'priest-thinker', who was surely going to arise in primitive societies as religion gradually arose, *mana* was not merely the strange or the frightening or the unexplained or the impressive, but the potency of the spirits behind the things.

In other words we are supposing that religion grew out of fear and awe and wonder; indeed, to be more specific, out of the personification of the unexplained, and so the 'magical', powers of nature. We are certainly on dangerous ground here; for the argument as to the difference between religion and the belief in magic, and whether the first emanated from the second, has been long and furious. The best that we can do is to try to sidestep it.

Sir James Frazer's argument was that man started with crude magic, almost wholly a naturalistic idea, a bastard science; he then, slowly realizing his mistake, changed from trying to force nature to bend to his will, to propitiating nature and supplicating the spirits that stood behind her. The objections to this theory however are first that primitives show little sign of realizing that magic does not work, their frame of mind being such that it either does work or seems to work, and secondly that even the most primitive peoples always do seem to have an idea of spiritual beings.

Perhaps to have a look at what is called *animism* will help us to resolve the difficulty. The word derives from *anima* which in Latin means 'breath'—what an *animal* possesses, being alive—hence also

177

'the soul'. Animism is therefore the belief that everything in nature has a soul or a personality. Now that belief can be anything from the crude and childlike idea that things must be alive just as you yourself are alive (resulting in anything from taboos and sympathetic magic to the petulant kicking of the stone that has 'kicked' you) to the much less materialistic idea, almost the Platonic idea if you like, that behind the apparent reality of material things is a greater reality of its spiritual essence—that there is a Spirit of the Stream and of the Woods and the Mountains and indeed perhaps one Great Spirit behind it all.

We can legitimately bring in the soul too, man's own soul.

For man dreams. Primitive peoples may well have dreamt more vividly than we do; at least, not possessing the printed word, they must have thought much more in visual images. Now two things happen when you dream: the dead walk; and, while your body lies inert, you yourself walk. Dreams therefore, and not only dreams but trances, natural or self-induced, and epileptic states and all such forms of dualism, must have done much to induce a belief both in an after-life for the dead—we have touched upon that already—and in man's possession of a soul. It is significant that in both Latin (*anima*) and Greek (*psyche*) the same word is used for 'breath' and for 'soul'. In sleep the soul may pass out from the mouth unless one takes the necessary magic precautions; at death it has already passed, but a shell from the rhythmic-breathing seashore may help if placed in the dead man's mouth—a practice observed by certain Stone Age men.

We see that there are many reasons for believing that man early acquired the concept of religion. How early he acquired it, and exactly how and why he did acquire it, we can leave to the experts to argue about—an interesting but an interminable argument. Indeed we can if we wish, and with a good show of reason, hold that there is no cause to adduce any explanation of why man became religious, since it was in his very nature to do so, being instinctively aware that he was different from the animals in the possession of his vivid, imaginative and restless brain, or 'saturated', to use Leslie Paul's[16] phrase, 'with a consciousness of the powers of the spiritual within him'.

Not that we must entertain the idea that Stone Age men were all

178

universal blends of poet and priest. If imaginative he was not impractical; he had to live.

We may return to the rites of initiation. If we wish to make a clear distinction between magic and religion we shall say that the one seeks to coerce nature and the other to influence or propitiate the spiritual beings behind nature. In any case both aspects can be seen clearly in all known examples of initiation ceremonies, the Mandan Indians' included. As to what evidence there is that by the time the hunting stage of early man's existence was fading into the Neolithic such rites were established, we have at least the shadows of the mutilated hands at Gargas, some evidence of circumcision in the pictures of men (which though significantly infrequent on the cave walls do add up in total to a tidy number, particularly if we include those scratched on bone and antler), and from the same source some considerable evidence of ritual dance.

Initiation ceremonies have a secular and practical purpose: to 'pass out' (to return to the military simile) the young men into full membership of the tribe. But they are religious ceremonies too. For they enlist spiritual guidance, and they seek to solemnize and impress. That, one might say, is the essential of primitive religion: to take those crucial occasions in the cycle of life of which we spoke (when quoting from Ruth Benedict in Chapter 13) and to release, and at the same time to exercise and to make memorable, those emotions. In the next chapter we will look at some further examples of Stone Age Man's probable ways of religious thought.

17

Life and More Life

To PUT it negatively, it would be very strange indeed if Stone Age Man was not concerned with

> Totems and taboos
> Rites of passage
> Ordeals
> Omens
> Propitiations
> Sacrifices.

The first we have dealt with. The second is a useful term covering all those rituals and customs that man has invented to mark the crucial occasions in the human journey: birth or entry into life; puberty, or as it were a second birth into that state which is responsible for the propagation of life; and death, the passing on to 'the undiscovered country'.

Paul Radin in a tough and unmystical book, *Primitive Religion*,[35] having described religion as 'the emotional correlate of the struggle for existence in our insecure physical and social environment', lists the occasions for its appearance as 'first, the physiological facts of birth, puberty, disease and death; second, the contact of man with the external world and the forces of nature; and third, the collision of man with man'. Let us use both his and my categories as a framework for this chapter.

Under Mr. Radin's first and my second category, there is something more to be said about what primitive man always seems to consider a most, if not the most, important occasion in the passage through life, puberty. The rites centring round the girl and not the boy are usually neither so important nor so elaborate, dull and

180

boring rather than exciting and terrifying. Her role in the life cycle will be the more fundamental but in a way the more passive. From the time of her first menstruation to her time of marriage and child-bearing—in all probability she has already been betrothed— she will be an object, a rather strange object, to be kept segregated and protected. Men have always been perhaps a little frightened as well as attracted by all aspects of femininity, and menstruation seems in particular to have appalled them. It was, we may believe, a *mana* that might debilitate them, that is to say the male and the physically strong one, by imparting some of the weakness of women; it must be shunned and guarded against by taboos—the girl, particularly on the first occasion, is in a dangerous spiritual state. The unoffending youngster then, or rather the offending, will be at once clapped into a hut by herself, even in the dark. There she will be specially attended. Besides not being allowed to see the sun she may well be prevented from setting foot upon the ground—more later of this and the reasons behind it. This incarceration may be a matter of days as described in Margaret Mead's *Growing Up in New Guinea* to a matter of years (*The Golden Bough*). It is naturally very much a woman's affair, as initiation ceremonies are a male. Men are excluded, not only from participation but from knowledge: all these puberty rites are great breeders of secrecy and secret societies. Margaret Mead tells how in the New Guinea society she studied the men assert solemnly that the females of their tribe never menstruate, for so their women-folk have told them.

But never let us think that primitive customs are wholly foolish or unpractical or that primitive ways of thought may be dismissed with indulgent laughter. After all, their ways of thought have lasted longer than ours, and sometimes it may be ours in our complicated and artificial civilization that to the proverbial Martian, or to God, appear the stranger. No doubt the young girl enjoyed the feasts that were wont to accompany the beginning of her puberty, no doubt she received from her jailer-attendants good advice, both practical and spiritual—good, that is, within the context of her tribal culture—as well as what seems to us heartless handling. She was no doubt impressed, which is the purpose of all rites: through her mind her future conduct had been guided into the way in which the collective wisdom of the tribe dictated.

．　　　．　　　．　　　．　　　．

The pangs of birth-giving need no impressing on the female mind; and to both the parents in a hard primitive life the occasion may seem all too frequent, certainly it will not be unique in a lifetime. The ceremonies therefore that cluster round this beginning of the passage through life do not seem to have been elaborate. This does not mean that the Stone Age *accouchement* would not have been a strange and significant scene to witness. It would almost certainly have seemed a bewildering mixture of the commendably practical and the utterly unreasonable. In *Primitive Heritage*[27] there is a description by one Matilda Stevenson of a childbirth among the Pueblo Indians, occurring 'at midnight, October 20, 1896'. The Pueblos were then living in something like a late Stone Age culture. There is much practical help on the part of the doctresses (mother-in-law and two grandmothers) present, some of which we should call perfectly sound, such as kneading and manipulation, some not so sound, such as blowing into the patient's mouth to help force the baby out. But there is also the bringing in of the 'officers of the Great Fire fraternity' to sing their incantations 'to the Beast Gods'— a modern district nurse would hardly welcome a glee club even if it did sing hymns. Many animals eat the afterbirth, and it has been suggested that early man did the same. It is much more likely that the mind and imagination got to work and that it became a symbol, as it has become in this instance: it is taken to the river and there thrown in, with a prayer for the blessed gift of many more children. There is much other symbolism: the mother bites on a stone, and it is white, so that the baby's teeth may be white and strong; a line of meal is sprinkled over the child's bed of sand, being the straight path it must follow in order to receive the blessings of the Sun Father and the Earth Mother. The baby is washed, but long prayers accompany the washing. . . .

Sickness also brings forth that same mixture at which we are likely to feel so impatient, of the admirably practical and the fantastically and even sinisterly mystical. We have cited the universal primitive belief that death is never natural, and the same must have applied to sickness and injury and accidents. Indeed there are no accidents. This is primitive man being not sillier than ourselves but less acquiescent in fate. He knows as well as we do that there is an immediate cause, and his efforts to alleviate the results may be as strictly practical—or nearly so. But there must be, he believes, a deeper cause: why is *this* man struck down? He will seek the answer in the evil designs of Nature and of men—and since all Nature is a manifestation of the power of spiritual beings and since man can influence Nature as Nature can influence man, he will in practice largely seek the cause of misfortune in the machinations of human beings.

In other words he believes in witchcraft. Now witchcraft is for us and our understanding a dangerous word to use, for it has so many overtones, so exclusively a connotation of evil. Man has always believed in witchcraft; indeed our Western civilization of the last mere two or three hundred years is unique in not believing in it. Witchcraft has led historically to great horror and cruelty, both in its extermination and its practice amongst the more decadent primitives. But with the original Primitive it was no more than the logical out-come—no, that is the wrong word, the imaginative outcome—of sympathetic magic, the power to influence at a distance, growing into a belief in the spiritual world behind the material and, once again, the power of man to influence and control those spirits. It is indeed supernatural; but not incomprehensibly supernatural, because as we have said supernatural and natural are to the untutored mind in-distinguishable.

The same may be said of the Witch Doctor, that it is a title liable to give an over-sinister impression. We will use another native word that the anthropologist has borrowed (Mongolian-Siberian this time), the *Shaman*, and we shall have something more to say of the Shaman after we have introduced the Neolithic Revolu-tion. But he must surely have begun to exist before the hunters disappeared and may well have entered pre-history in the person of the cave artist. Turn the coin and his image becomes that of the 'poet-thinker', whose existence and growth we have also presupposed.

In all sickness and deathbed scenes then we may believe to have been present the thought of witchcraft and the person of the witch doctor. At the worst he flocked round like the vulture, at the best he effected by faith and power and prayer and personality a cure. Once again it was a mixture of the good and bad, of the sensible and absurd, the terrifying and the benign. The evil influence—so said in effect the shamans—we will discover and exorcize and so set the patient's mind at rest. But let us at the same time rub him down and give him a nauseous draught that will make him sweat or be sick. Let us also pray. If the spirits so will it, he will recover.

That is not an entirely bad way of looking at things.

But is it religion? Certainly religion enters into it and into all we have described, that is if we accept the definition of it as 'the emotional correlate of the struggle for existence' or our earlier 'belief in spiritual beings superior to man'. Not that man, though frightened, was entirely humble in this matter: even if there were superior spirits he could hardly yet persuade himself that he could not control them.

By his own light, primitive man may even be said to have shown more logic and consistency than ourselves; certainly he sometimes had more faith. This is apparent in his use and acceptance of ordeals. These are the sovereign method of proving innocence or guilt, with the added advantage that if guilt is proved the punishment has already, partially or wholly, been given. Travellers' and anthropologists' reports abound with wondering descriptions of primitive peoples' ordeal ceremonies and of their universally cheerful willingness to undergo them. There is the walking over fire, the plunging of the arm into boiling water, the taking of poison, a poison that can kill. The willingness stems from an 'unscientific' but highly religious conviction that, for instance, the poison is quite simply a different thing if the partaker is innocent: its *mana*, its spiritual content, will in that case be harmless. Often of course the ordeal must have achieved its object, not by magic, but by means of primitive man's simplicity of mind and intensity of emotion, and so by his powers to control consciously those bodily reactions that are normally subconscious. The fire did not burn, the water did not scald, the poison was sicked up.

The real point about the ordeal is that in the most primitive societies it constitutes pretty well the sole sanction that exists to enforce what we call law and order—that and the public opinion that goes with it. The guilty man—if not already dead from the poison—will be ostracized, will be suffused with a shame only to be removed by some act of expiation. He has committed not so much a crime as a sin, and a sin against the tribe, which is the greatest sin—that is why, you will remember, incest is more reprehensible than murder. We are now in fact already in the realm of Mr. Radin's third kind of producer of religious feeling—we will for our convenience reverse his order—the collision of man with man. It is a surprising discovery of the anthropologist that in the most primitive societies, the sort of society in which we may believe our late paleolithic and mesolithic hunters existed, the need for law and the need for the policeman hardly exist. The place of the former is taken largely by the force of custom, of the latter and of all that goes with him by the shaman, the ordeal, and public opinion. There exists what has been called a 'closed' society. In it one is a member of the clan, and nothing else matters; one obeys its rules and hardly entertains the idea of not obeying. But if the flesh in spite of all is weak, then the wrath of the tribe and of the ancestral spirits of the tribe, working through the mystical and unseen power in things, will find you out and your fate is sealed and irrevocable. The religious aspect is all-pervading and cannot be separated from the secular; in fact 'secular' has not yet found a meaning.

There is another property of the unseen powers. If they can be the instrument of retribution can they not also be the instruments of beneficence? There is a difficulty here. The trouble is really twofold: how to know what the spirits are going to do, and how to see to it that what they do is what you want them to do. We come back to Mr. Radin's second category—man's contact with the forces of nature, and to our remaining categories of Stone Age human concern: omens and propitiations and sacrifices.

Araigné de matin, chagrin; araigné de soir, espoir; it's unlucky to see the new moon through glass; salute a single magpie in your path! Our superstitions are a relic, or rather a continuation, of man's intense desire to know the future and to control it. He can *think* into the future—a wonderful and entertaining ability. Why then can he not *see* into the future, and *make* the future? Perhaps if he exercises his imagination sufficiently he can. Luck is heart-rendingly, frustratingly fickle; but it can be exploited, and turned.

First omens. Here we can at least understand and sympathize with primitive man; or if we cannot we are singularly self-deceptive. It would be amazing if the ancient hunter had not believed in omens. But the things he believed in are sometimes very strange.

He was, no doubt, most expert in observing the physical signs of the hunt: the displaced twig, the recent spoor, the tell-tale behaviour of birds and of other beasts. But what he wanted was something more. And since everything had behind it its spirit it could hardly be

185

lacking—anything unusual would *mean* something. In particular he wanted to know if luck would be going his way: was it a good day on which to start a hunt, or should he call the whole thing off?

Something comes up suddenly on your right. Right is your powerful and skilful side. Good, all right! But left? Left, as the Romans had it, was *sinister*. Birds have often been the embodiment of omen: perhaps because they do rise up so startlingly, perhaps because so transparently they are themselves emotional beings, perhaps simply because having wings that can take them up to the firmament they have always been regarded as spiritual and often as the repository of man's soul—there was, if you remember, von Koenigswald's interpretation of the hunting scene of Lascaux. Indeed in Sarawak it is reported that the word for omen is 'bird', *burong;* and to obtain an omen (a nice bit of grammatical construction), *beburong*. This is quoted by Lévy-Bruhl in his book *Primitive Mentality*.[34] He goes on to quote from another traveller in the district:

'The Kenyah of Tanah Putih wished to make use of our stay to build a boat. But on entering the forest (to fell a tree) they met a *hisit* (bird) which whistled to the left of them, and they turned right about. Half an hour afterwards they returned and felled a tree, but at the moment it fell they again perceived an unfavourable augury. They left the tree lying, and gave up all idea of their boat.'

That is the trouble. Omens multiply alarmingly, and you tend never to do anything. They also become highly involved: multiple omens that need an expert to interpret them. Man tortures himself with ingenious complications.

He goes further, considerably further. His next step is to produce an omen artificially; he can never act until he knows his fate, and he is impatient. He therefore invents things: 'if I pour out this libation and it soaks in quickly my project will be fortunate'. Or he will rake over his dreams, and invest them with significance. Dreams are always potent to the primitive mind and likely to be invested too, as we have seen, with belief in the continued existence of the dead. Omen-seeking therefore takes on a tinge of ancestor worship, or at least of spirit worship. Many savage peoples seek to induce their dreams and visions; they do it by starvation and self-torture, by going, as did a greater man after them, out into the wilderness. What the spirits there tell them will be their guide.

From that to propitiation. The spirits will give omens, and one must of course play fair and observe the rules of interpretation. But what one wants, and wants so passionately, is a good omen—in fact a blessing from the spirits. One propitiates therefore, makes an offering, an oblation: a heap of salt; a pouring of water or—if you have invented it—of beer or wine; the killing of a bird or beast. Then one may with the more confidence seek interpretation in one's dreams or in some invented sign or portent. A favourite portent, as all know, one that continued even into Roman civilization, was the

The ancestor. Modelled skull
from Jericho

condition of the entrails of the bird or beast that had been sacrificed. That is gruesome and to us incomprehensible. But I do not think we need impute any sinister motives to the practitioners—nothing more than a consuming desire, a tradition-bound and inescapable super-stition, a lack of squeamishness (which in all things we may im-pute to early man) and the simple fact that they had to find something on hand with which to interpret. No doubt, to be unsqueamish our-selves, a newly disincorporated liver does show most subtle variations in hue and condition.

Another untenderness of mind brings us back to ancestor wor-ship or at least ancestor-using in the way of blessings and omens. There is very often among primitive peoples a tremendous pre-occupation with skulls. They are carried about; they are set up and consulted, they are decorated and painted—such have been found in neolithic Jericho—and given a new coat of paint when they are about to be consulted; offerings are made to them. The practice is reasonable, or rather, within its ambit of acceptance of the power of the dead, percipient. For in the skull once lay the seat of the intelligence, and if anywhere the seat of the soul. Man, I think, must have had a terrific ambivalence towards the dead: he loathed and loved them; he was afraid and he was proud; he was kind to them, and if they did not reciprocate he would bully them. Skulls and bones had a fascination for him, though I doubt whether it was such a horrified fascination as we might imagine. Certainly they had a great religious significance for him. He set them up and importuned them and sacrificed to them. For prediction and for blessing he sacrificed to the spirits in general—just possibly to one supreme spirit in particular.

And with that brief mention of the art and custom of sacrifice we will end this chapter—but not our concern with sacrifice.

We have sketched those customs and observances of the hunting folk that seem probable and can be called religious. No one is going to suggest that all of these early people observed all these kinds of custom and belief: we do well to remind ourselves of Ruth Benedict's Dionysian and Apollonian peoples, even to our modern categories of introvert and extrovert, and of the fact that there must always have been degrees of religiosity both in individuals and in societies. However, some of the people must have done some of these things, tortured themselves physically and spiritually in these ways, gladdened themselves with these feasts and observances and communal rites. Evidence of it? Things of the spirit do not leave much that is material, and we can only turn again to the cave paintings and the other works of art, to the burials and the evidence of care for the dead, the weapons and ornaments and food left in their graves. Once again perhaps we may think of that strange nest of severed skulls at Ofnet.

In particular two things are significant, one of which has intentionally not been mentioned before. The first is that some of the paleolithic etchings on bone and ivory and most of the little models are of the female figure with the feminineness much exaggerated— the classical example is the ludicrously, or engagingly, voluptuous Venus of Willendorf. These are often called 'cult objects', which is meaningless, or 'fertility cult objects', which is misleading. Man was not obsessed with fertility as such, nor was he outstandingly lascivious, rather the reverse. He wanted life, and more life, and more abundant life, which is not quite the same thing.

The discovery so far not mentioned is of the reindeer hunters as they began to follow their quarry for the last time slowly towards the North. The site is Meiendorf near Hamburg, that marvellously strategic site; the date, by pollen analysis, is round about 15,000 B.C., a little later than the Lascaux paintings. In the deepest part of the lake which Alfred Rust and his team had been draining was

Fecundity. Figurine from Grimaldi and
etching on bone from Předmost

found the entire skeleton of a two-year-old reindeer doe; and wedged inside the cavity of its ribs was a large stone weighing nearly twenty pounds. This is the comment, a fair one I think, of Geoffrey Bibby[10] in his description of the find:

'It was impossible to mistake the significance of this discovery. There could be no other reason for sinking in the waters of the lake the entire carcass of a prime reindeer than sacrifice. The same feeling as that which induced the ancient Greeks to spill a drop or two of wine from the beaker as an offering to the gods before drinking must here have persuaded the Ice Age hunters to offer the first and the best of their booty to the gods, which, they must have felt, were omnipresent in the vicinity of their encampment.'

18

The Neolithic Revolution

NATURE is both prolific and competitive. If given the chance almost any form of life will increase in something very near to geometrical progression: 2, 4, 8, 16, 32; 3, 9, 27, 81, 243. But there are so many forms of life competing for the sun and the air and the food which is often each other, that over long periods no single form ever gets the chance to show what it can do: the grim balance which we study under the term ecology comes into play. So far man was no exception. He had increased, but with painful slowness. In great tracts of mountain and jungle and forest and swamp he did not exist at all; even over his favourite grounds you could surely have wandered for days and met none of his species. Over the whole face of the globe probably only a very few millions existed, perhaps less.

But if the science of ecology is observed and practised, if some forms of life are given by man's hand a special chance and competition eliminated, then the picture at once becomes very different. The favoured life can increase, 'some an hundredfold, some sixty-fold, some thirtyfold'—and the life that by its skill and thought has created this favour, man's life, can reap the benefit. You can make a beginning in this process by finding the plant that has edible seeds of a worthwhile size and by weeding round it. Or you can control the herd so that you steer it not into a death-trap but so that other depredators are warned off and it increases both in size and friendliness.

'Control' is the essential word in both instances. So far man has merely been one of the predators, albeit a particularly efficient one—there is no other known reason why for instance mammoth should not still be browsing happily in Siberia. But now he is going to augment food-finding with food-producing, and gradually shift the burden of his life from one to the other. From a parasite on nature he will become a partner. Like Adam he becomes a gardener. And his sons become either farmers or herdsmen—and as with Cain and Abel there will be rivalry between them.

But that is going too fast. No one really knows who started agriculture, or the domestication of animals (beyond the dog). We can however make some very intelligent guesses—and we guess that the same people did not invent both.

The two do seem to have arrived at somewhere the same time in prehistory. That is not surprising: there is this urge to find a new way to prosperity, caused by a warmer and drier world, by the pressure of the creeping forest and the expanding desert. Perhaps the growing of crops has the better claim to priority in time and so we will give it priority here.

In a way man is now more of a predator than ever. He goes straight to the heart of the plant's continuing life, the embryonic next generation, the seed. He is wise of course, for that is where lies and is likely to lie the greatest nourishment. He must show further wisdom and restraint however, some equivalent of the close season that the hunter observes. He must store and not eat some of the grain. He must prepare a plot, and scatter the seed on the ground, and protect it from other predators, and let it grow up into a plant again and produce more food. This to us is elementary. To early man it was an awe-inspiring partnership in a continuing miracle.

Agriculture and food producing means primarily the growing of corn, wheat and barley in the old world, maize in the new: here is the food that is going to give sustained energy—a carnivore fluctuates between ferocious activity, gorging, and sleep—and that is going to make the building of a food reserve possible. One can lay down pretty closely the prerequisites for the discovery and successful use of wheat and barley and see whither one is led. This is what Professors Peake and Fleure do in their book *Peasants and Potters*,[32] and we will follow them. First the location must be one where the seed will not only grow wild but ripen easily and quickly—in fact spectacularly, for man, conservative man, needs to be struck forcibly with an idea before he will accept it. It will be an area then of a regular and assured sequence of rain and strong sunshine. It will not be in forest land for man has not yet learnt to make appreciable clearings. It is likely however to be in a fairly restricted area, where man will not be wandering off before he ever fully appreciates the plant's generous cycle. It will also help if there is present the cross-fertilization of human cultures that may break down the terrific wall of taboos and 'don't ever do anything different!' that must have existed in the Stone Ages—we need only

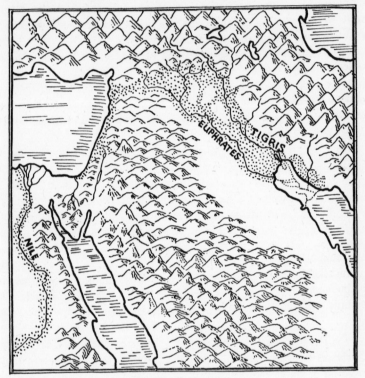

The Fertile Crescent

to remember such an isolated and self-sufficient group as the kitchen-middeners huddled along the sea-shore.

With all this in mind our gaze becomes focused inevitably on what the great American prehistorian and orientalist, J. H. Breasted, christened so very aptly the 'Fertile Crescent'. It runs as a great arch or crescent above the Arabian desert, its left resting in the lower Nile Valley and Palestine, its centre in Syria and Kurdistan, its right in Iraq along the double valley of the Tigris and Euphrates. It is semi-fertile now; it was very fertile then. It is protected on the outside by the sea and a ring of mountains, on the inside to some extent by the desert. It constitutes the cradle of civilization.

Just where in this crescent corn-harvesting began—though it is admittedly a big span, of 1500 miles or more—can I think be left to the experts to dispute. Similarly which came first, wheat or barley and which wheat was the first, emmer, the two-berried or split wheat, or on the other hand *Triticum vulgare*, ordinary or soft wheat. What matters is that people of the mountain slopes may have met here the probably equally hungry people from the growing desert and together they met the wild corns and recognized them for what they were worth. At Mount Carmel on the Palestine coast and at Jericho in the Jordan valley they took their microliths such as had existed since Azilian times, or made curved saw-edged blades, and fitted them into sickles. Now we have found the sickles, after

The neolithic sickle

anything up to nine thousand years; and there is shown on them the unmistakable sheen of cut grasses. And, since only cranks like Nebuchadnezzar eat grass, and not for long, we can pretty safely assume that the grasses cut had edible seeds at the top of them.

No animal will consent to domestication that is not loved, whose confidence is not gained. That must have happened with the dog. And though we look on sheep and cattle very differently I doubt if the Neolithic people did; they were to them dear possessions, emotionally as well as economically: recall the one ewe lamb and the one lost sheep out of a hundred which will be sought until it is found. The ancient hunters respected their quarry and felt a mystical brotherhood with it; but something more than that is wanted now, and when Professors Peake and Fleure in the book to which we have already referred suggest that it would be no fierce hunting people who were first responsible for this second great step forward but 'a people of mild and gentle manners' they have I think made a likely and striking point. They suggest as such people

193

'hill folk of a central mountain range' and as the recurring scene of the taming a wooded and parkland region between the Fertile Crescent and the steppe lands to the north. At the breeding season, they imagine, the cow might well wander off up a lush and fertile valley. There a human mother might meet a bovine one, and entice her to share her milk. So would arrive the second miracle that so impressed the people who witnessed and accomplished it: the great Cow Mother who fed the human race. No doubt it was not all sweetness and light and sometimes there was some coercion in it, the lasso or the corral. But if ever the cow was to stay of her own free will, and the bull to visit her, there would have to be some animal trust in human motives—and even if there is a killing in the end nevertheless the herd that is humanly protected does on balance benefit.

Actually there are two more or less distinct ways of life based on animal husbandry; what we should call dairy farming, and pastoralism. In the first the cattle are kept primarily for their milk, and their care will be combined with crop-raising, the beasts benefiting from the by-products. But the pastoralist, whether of cattle or sheep or horses, is dependent almost wholly on his animals; he is interested in meat and hide and wool as well as milk and he is not concerned with the coddling of a few cows in a byre. It is the latter who is the essential nomad, ever 'seeking new pastures'.

Thus then a double revolution, almost a triple. Yet it is of course fair to call it a single one. For whether it be dairying or crop-raising or herd-tending the essential step is food production instead of food chasing, a partnership with nature instead of a battening upon her. We need now to ask ourselves: what is going to be the effect?

The answer quite simply is, terrific. The inventions that flow from the change constitute a formidable list. Man now is going to have the leisure as well as the incentive to make them. His life has been changed. Very slowly, but with acceleration, he begins to become modern man. He turns now, it has been strikingly said, from being a savage to become a barbarian. Of course neither epithet has a complimentary sound and both are commonly used with a condescending and pejorative sort of connotation: you may not think there is much to choose between the two. But there is. The savage is as it were the wild man of the woods; the barbarian on the other hand is one of ourselves, though of course a foreigner without culture, without our culture that is to say. It is no longer a matter of 'there but for the grace of God go I' but 'there goes my cultural ancestor'.

The preliminary processes of the change are slow, that is the point to make at this stage. Even where it all began the archaeological discoveries show that corn-growing (or it may only have been corn-gathering) was for a long time no more than a way of supplementing, of eking out, the food that is hunted. As for the domestication of animals it is obviously a change by imperceptible degrees from hunting them, through hunting-and-herding, through herding, to full-scale controlling and breeding. The discoveries made at the sites of two different cultures, called respectively the Natufian and the Tasian, will serve to show the sort of thing that was happening. The first is typically found at Mount Carmel, already mentioned as the site of the grass-polished sickle (the other site mentioned, Jericho, which is startling in its significance, we will leave to the end of this chapter). The second has its home near to the Nile valley, typically at Badari and a district already known as the breeding ground of pre-pleistocene apes, the Fayum.*

The Natufians of Mount Carmel were a small people not much more than five feet in height, whose tribal badge seems to have been the knocking out of the eye teeth, who decked themselves with necklaces and girdles, and who reverently buried their dead. They fished with hook-and-line and harpoon, and they had micro-lithic arrows: a typical 'mesolithic' hunting and fishing culture in fact. But beside that sickle with the sheen on it were found pestles and mortars, presumably for grinding the corn, and the sort of flint that would be used as a hoe. The same sort of Natufian sickles have been found at the lowest levels of a site in North Persia, at Tepe Sialk, where the excavations show signs of hunting by slings and clubs—David and Goliath combined—mixed however with the keeping of cattle and sheep and goats and the spinning of some fibre or fibres unknown.

The Fayum site in the same way could be called a kitchen midden. But here there was discovered straw-lined pits in which

* Much of the information for this chapter is taken from the late Professor Gordon Childe's *New Light on the Most Ancient East.*[36]

had been stored emmer wheat and barley—and the barley was a cultivated sort and not a wild. 'Saddle querns' were found, that is the 'nether' stone of a hand mill for grinding the corn, worn by the upper stone into the slightly dished shape of a saddle. Flax also must have been grown, and there are definite traces of the weaving of a coarse linen.

The Badarians had saddle querns too. They buried their dead wrapped in skins and in straw coffins lowered into pits—a kind of storage?—and they were growing flax and weaving a little linen. They had pottery, as had all these cultures, flat-bottomed and not pointed like the Danish kitchen-midden folk, and yielding to the archaeologists in this instance one sample of the 'beaker', the equivalent of our tumbler, which is going to turn up significantly in Europe centuries later. They made crude little ivory figures and they had palettes for eye-painting, that universal custom of these climes which is partly utilitarian as a protection against glare, partly adornment and—if we accept the greenness of the malachite that they used as a symbol of growth and wellbeing and fertility—perhaps partly magic. Magic or symbolism—and the primitive mind would make no distinction—is evident in the adornment of a tribe living a little further north, at Merimde, and also of the people of Jericho; they were necklaces of miniature axe-heads—potent as well as pleasing.

Finally: the earliest people of Jericho, or at any rate the earliest so far discovered. Here the recent finds made by Dr. Kathleen Kenyon[37] and her band of experts have been upsetting some previously held opinions. For one thing these people had no pottery, although they were obviously much more advanced than the 'mesolithic' kitchen-midden people who had some—which goes to show that these divisions of the Stone Age must be used as it were only loosely and with circumspection. For another, though they were truly only in the early stages of the neolithic, still using arrows for hunting as well as querns for grinding corn, these people were yet making themselves mud-bricks and with them solid and quite spacious one-storey houses in such numbers that the conglomeration has as much claim to be called a town as a village. They had found an ideal site—fertile alluvial soil, a baking sun, and the saving grace of a perennial spring of water—and they were making the most of it.

196

They were thrusting ahead of all competitors though later—there is sign of catastrophe and massacre—falling back and starting again on a reduced scale more in line with the other cultures that we have already described.

Two things, I think, stand out about these early people of Jericho. The first is, how excellent were their houses. There soon arrive hard and highly polished floors that even curve up to the walls in what we thought was a very modern effort at hygiene, and there are found polishing-stones for other purposes: the proud housewife has obviously been born. Secondly these people practised that particular form of ancestor worship, or importuning of them or whatever it is, that shows itself in an obsessional manipulation of the skulls. The Jerichoan most skilfully and artistically remodelled on to them a face of clay.

Now let us finish this chapter by making one or two things very clear.

Typically neolithic: the flint that is ground and polished. For this axe-head the wooden handle has been reconstructed

We are talking so far of only the beginnings of the Neolithic Revolution: full-scale agriculture or pastoralism is not yet; historical Egypt and Sumer are a long way ahead. The last Ice Age finally disappears about 10,000 B.C. and warmth and dryness begin to come; these cultures we have described date between about 7000 and 5000 B.C. Neolithic Man flourishes and is established in the Middle East during the fifth and fourth millenia.

But in Europe the Neolithic Age proper will not even begin until about 3000 B.C. It is not a period in history between fixed dates; it is a period in the evolution of men *through which they pass*.

The Neolithic Age was essentially, as its name implies, a new way of working stone: typically now, flints (and other kinds of stone) are ground and polished. This is not an outmoded differentiation, in spite of the fact that it has not previously been mentioned at all, in spite of the fact that the really important thing about the neolithic is a way not of working flint but of earning a living. The typical neolithic tool is the ground and polished axe or celt, grandfather one might say of the iron celt that gave its name later to a people. Some were found at Badari, but there were not many in those early Eastern cultures, and for the very good reason that they were not much needed.

The heavy neolithic polished axe is the tree feller *par excellence*. That is why it does truly represent the new age. For over Europe-Asia the forests are encroaching; and before agriculture can flourish the trees will have to be felled.

19

Man Settles Down

IT IS hard to say whether man is innately a home-maker or a wanderer. He seems to be both. Born with an habitual cussedness, or a divine discontent, he wants a home when he is wandering and to wander when he has a home.

At any rate the desire for a permanent home is there. The woman in particular, having her baby, about to have her baby, bringing up her baby, must have longed for one: we have seen at Jericho how soon house-pride arrived. But in paleolithic times the opportunity hardly arose—where your food wandered you wandered. Now the opportunity was presenting itself, not often at the opening of the Neolithic Age one would imagine but at what may be called its second stage. That is when the tyro agriculturist has progressed beyond mere crop-snatching or the practice of exhausting the soil and passing on.

Both for man and his crops two essentials are needed: sunshine and water. Sunshine was not lacking, at least where agriculture began. Rain was not in all places so plentiful, though one could always pray for it or try to magic it. More helpful were oases and perpetual springs. Best of all were the big rivers in the wide valleys that once a year with wonderful precision flooded out on to the land. Outstandingly the Nile and the twin rivers Tigris and Euphrates did that—the latter on one occasion at least too beneficently, so that there was no forgetting the Flood. Besides irrigation however there was needed revitalization, the return to the ground of its necessary goodness. In the more favoured spots perhaps a little of allowing to lie fallow and the very sparseness of the crop—the plough was not yet invented—would be enough. Burning of stubble and the manuring by cattle, either naturally or by the age-old, though now new, practice of muck-spreading, would have the desired result. But best of all, once more the broad rivers would do that for you, for with the flooding would come new earth, silt from the higher reaches of the river.

Yet there were two disadvantages to be overcome in the broad river valleys. They needed, in varying degrees, to be initially drained and the irrigating floods had to be controlled and directed. Secondly their very fertility was a disadvantage: every flint, virtually every piece of wood, had to be imported from without, only mud and more mud being at your disposal. People overcame these disadvantages of course, for the incentive to do so was overwhelming. But there was needed for it some considerable *social organization*. It was for this reason no doubt that the beginnings of the Neolithic Revolution were slow; it was for this reason that the civilizations of the Nile and the Tigris-Euphrates were probably later in starting than such sites of the village-round-the-spring as Jericho.

However, do not let us think in terms of particular localities as yet. From now on, cultures are spreading and growing and differentiating wildly, and this is perhaps almost the last time that we shall be able to generalize. It is surely enough to know what were man's inventions and triumphs as he began to settle down to a village life without having to consider in each instance just where the advance was made. Often for that matter the knowledge is implicit: one makes mud bricks where there is mud, and log huts where there are forest trees to fell. Also do not forget that we shall be ranging over a fair-sized time period as well as over space. Relatively there is a tremendous acceleration; but we are still comparing with the paleolithic when a way of making a hand-axe could last a quarter of a million years. Even now, before the Stone Age begins to make way for the Age of Metals, we have at least a couple of thousand years on our hands.

Slow change then, in the face of the disapproval of the Elders, and of taboo, and of iron custom; agonizing reappraisals; nevertheless, change and progress all the time. It was wonderful what a difference this new aggressive policy, this active partnership with nature, was effecting: geometrical progression was not your enemy but your friend. What with the children helping to tend and mind the animals and the crops growing miraculously on their own— once you had planted and done the proper rituals of course—you really had time on your hands and time to think. So had your wife.

There was primarily the building of a house, a house not a hut. So far a favourite method of seeking protection, where the ground would allow it, had been to dig a round shallow pit, to erect a roof-tree in the centre, and to place branches and turf, or woven wattles and daubed mud, around it. But now men built walls from the ground upwards, first of mud, then of hand-made bricks dried in the sun and then with bricks of mud and a binding of straw that were made as we do in a mould. They used what was to hand and were intelligent about it. When Neolithic men fanned out and with their polished stone adzes and axes began to hew down the forest they naturally found a use for the tree-trunks.* Their method would be something like this. Take the straight trunks of fir or pine and

The first brick of Jericho: sun-dried, unbaked, hand-made. Along the top are thumb marks for keying with the mud-mortar. Dr. Kenyon says they make a wall quite hard to demolish

lop off the branches. Lay two parallel to one another on the ground, the ends preferably on flat stones. Lay two shorter ones across their ends. Repeat this alternately until the height of a man is reached, then lay lighter trunks across the two walls and cover with grass and mud. Do that and you will have a log cabin. Improvements will no doubt come. Grooves will be made where the logs intersect; half timbers will form the roof, which in rainy climates will be given a slope; after erection a door—at first perhaps you burrowed under to enter—and even a window would be hacked out. Here without exaggeration was the beginning of architecture; and here certainly was the beginning of carpentry.

The possession of a house must have accentuated tremendously that need that we pampered moderns can hardly imagine being difficult to fill: for containers. The building of the hut itself, that is of the wattle and daub variety, may even have given ideas; or per-

* An adze is an axe with its line of blade at right angles to the handle, as with a draw-hoe. Wood needs splitting as much as cutting; the tool needs to be heavy and unbrittle as well as sharp. Many neolithic axes were made of igneous rock.

haps it was the other way about, baskets before wattle. Certainly plaiting and weaving is a practice with most varied possibilities. Then just possibly the mud daubed on the wattle may have furnished an idea. Charles Lamb wrote an essay on how man learnt to roast pig by the accidental burning down of his house with the pig inside. In sober truth man may have learnt the art of pottery in the same way: the roof of a burnt hut had become durable. Certainly some early pottery shows the marks of the withies that were within it, and much early pottery shows patterning that is obviously a copy of basket work: it is the old story, so striking in our own early motor-cars, of new inventions copying unnecessarily forms of the old. Pottery is not new; but now it is bursting forth and proliferating in an exuberance and variety which is like the evolution of a species

A memory of basket work: neolithic pot
found at Mortlake-on-Thames

speeded up to the nth degree. The shape has infinite variety; so has the patterning. Indeed it is here that Neolithic Man begins to show that the human race really is inherently artistic and that the cave painters were not a sort of inexplicable and unrepeatable miracle. This is a new art, of form and pattern, but it is a real and live one. The fact that every tribe and culture had its own tradition in pottery making, and always a slowly but traceably changing tradition, causing as it has done their wares to become the archaeologist's favourite tool for dating and categorizing, has rather killed our ability to look at neolithic pottery with a single and unbored and appreciative eye. It is certainly the more rewarding way to look if it can be managed.

But to return to the practical. Essentially it was *storage* that man wanted: not only to cook things but to keep things; not only

202

to put things in but to keep things out—out of the mouths of the greedy and the improvident. We come here to something much more widely important than the wife's store cupboard. Here is the beginning at last of something a little like Economic Man. If you can accumulate a *communal* reserve then you have made the greatest step forward, you have begun to emancipate your community from immediate, utterly and degradingly immediate, dependence upon nature. If agriculture is going to be anything more than a supplement to a hunting way of life, then there has got to exist a communal store of some sort to tide over from one harvest to the next. The greater the reserve, the more successful the community. And not only the greater but the better controlled: with economics is going to grow the need for authority, even the authority of the One Head Man. For the store adequate to tide over from one season to the next is not enough; what will be wanted is the strong and wise man who can persuade or force a community to save up in the fat years for the lean ones that will surely come. Joseph's Pharaoh did it, though that story is a long way ahead. But it is very significant that even the early Tasians had straw-lined pits for their grain.

Let us come back to the more personal, to the housewife in fact. Pottery gave great opportunity for cooking. Or rather perhaps cooking was becoming a necessity. It must have been a most encouraging discovery that the starchy cells of the cereal grains expanded under heat and were then so much more edible and nourishing. Hence not only the cook-pot but the quern. Flour has arrived. Bread has arrived.

That is an optimistic exaggeration. The 'army biscuit' has arrived, what the boy scout calls 'damper' has arrived; but hardly bread. It did arrive however, and probably, judging by the fact that all present similar 'barbarians' seem to have it, in neolithic times. With it would come beer: controlled fermentation with the aid of yeast. That extraordinary non-chlorophyll-making plant, with its capacity to create alcohol and give off carbon dioxide as it feeds on sugar, is, without either any coyness or blasphemy, surely describable as one of the great gifts of man from God. The tumbler-shaped *beaker*, already mentioned, gave its name to a people, so prolifically and typically is it found; it is reasonable to suppose that there would not have been so many beakers if there had been no beer.

Beer then to ferment; and milk to keep cool; and oil to store when the olive came to be cultivated; and spices perhaps, to be kept separate and ready for use. But it was not only the storing and cooking of foods that progressed; there was the discovery of new foods. Besides the cereals—wheat and barley and millet in their due season and climate, the mud-loving rice and the enormous-headed maize—there were the roots, manioc and yam and potato, and the fruits, the apple to be improved in Europe, the peach and apricot in Persia. The point is that man, having once learnt the trick, did not gather but cultivated. The same with his animals. He began to geld (a pleasanter word than castrate) and so to create for himself a tamer male animal. He began to breed, selectively. Charles Darwin in collecting evidence for one side of his great argument, artificial as opposed to natural selection, spent years amassing a mountain of facts from the farmers and gardeners and stock-breeders of his acquaintance: that was the lore of a triple profession which certainly went back to neolithic times, and the size of it now does surely give an indication of the size of it near to the beginning. Man must have been learning at a prodigious rate compared with the past—and exchanging his knowledge, a little cagily at times perhaps, and mixing his knowledge too no doubt, and as we shall see, with superstition and portentous mumbo-jumbo and ritual and worse.

Men learnt to grow and breed and adapt for other things than food. The thing-that-bound and the thing-that-plaited must always have been useful to him: withies, hair, sinews. Now he is going to make the most cheering strides forward. Both plant and animal are to help him; and whether the fuzz of the cotton plant and flax led him to sheep's wool or vice versa is hard to say. Perhaps it was the first, for wild sheep would need some adaptation by breeding before their hairy fleece would be of much use. We talk distantly and a little patronizingly of the distaff, and forget what a wonderfully inventive use of a wonderful phenomenon it was. The phenomenon is that fibres if skilfully twisted inexplicably change their nature and become a continuous thread. The invention is the spindle whorl to impart the necessary twisting motion. Many museums show the evolution of spinning and most curators will be willing to explain the process—showing you in all probability a spindle whorl that is neolithic. Weaving is perhaps a more obvious invention, that is to people who are already making baskets and mats. But the loom with its frame and its row of weights to keep the warp tight, such as Penelope used so patiently and disingenuously, is a clever and fairly complicated piece of furniture—and Penelope if not neolithic barbarian was only at the next stage, of Bronze Age Heroics.

What else? There must have been progress in means of transport, for before the Neolithic Age is ended man has spread pretty well over the whole earth. The boat and the raft must have improved

Distaff and spindle whorl

considerably, and the first sails were hoisted—to gladden the forbidding seascape for man, to uplift his spirit, and to afford him unlimited scope for technical mystery. On land the progress is not so great as might be expected. The wheel is definitely not yet, though the sledge is, used no doubt for sliding over mud or grass or sand as well as snow. The horse has not yet been saddled or bridled; he waits for the heroic age. But the ass has already become at least a beast of burden; perhaps too the camel.

And all this is in a *stone* age. That we must not forget: the fact should serve both to curb our admiration and enthusiasm lest we credit too much and at the same time to justify them since so much has been achieved. We have gone forward a long way in this rapid survey of neolithic inventions, and we might even be excused by sticklers for exactitude of having gone too far and strayed out of the Stone Age altogether. The trouble is of course that the people whose ways of life we are trying to recall do not oblige us with exactitude. They too strayed, very gradually from a use of stone, through a regard for any copper they might pick up (and a passion for gold), through the forging, smelting and casting of copper, through a similar use of bronze (copper hardened by an introduction of a small percentage of other metal, usually tin) and so to the discovery of iron. Not only is this process gradual but it might be called haphazard and at times almost half-hearted: men loved their old tools and, what is important, found them also a good deal cheaper. Archaeologists speak nowadays of a chalcolithic, a copper-stone, age; but the distinction does not seem of great significance and, even more than usual with these categories, no one can say when it began and ended. Sumeria and Egypt are as we said in the offing, and Crete and Assyria too, when the use of metals has really arrived and there have arrived too city-states, and priests and kings, and power, and slaves, and writing. The Neolithic leads up to all that, borders that, foreshadows that, but no more. It is a definite way of life of its own, aware of metals, perhaps a little fascinated by metals, but not really using metals—rather as we, in a somewhat accelerated way, are living an old way of life on the brink of the Atomic Age. Men must have liked their Stone Age peasant-villager-farmer way of life for it lasted one may say just about a thousand years in all places, of course not the same thousand and continuing when other places had already passed on to better or at least different horizons. Men even seem to have liked it so much, and the beliefs that went with it, that they finally set out to spread it across half the world.

One look before we follow them at a culture in its land of origin that we can call wholly neolithic, fully established as a primitive farming community. It will be a sample, no more; for now the dug sites at our disposal become embarrassingly many and none, naturally, are quite the same. We will take the Amratians.

The Amratians lived on the Nile in Upper Egypt north of Luxor and south of the site of Badari. They are the successors to the Tasians and perhaps their descendants; and having as it were served their apprenticeship in the desert outskirts they have come down to the more fertile but more exacting environment of the river valley to start the cultivation of the swampy and perennially flooding Nile.

They have left a good deal to tell us about themselves: their funerary vases and ornaments as well as their bones. They were a smallish people again, slight and small-skulled—not negroid and probably straight-haired.* The men are shown as clean-shaven except for a long pointed beard. The women seem to have begun that practice, so familiarly depicted in Egyptian scenes and traceable to Sumeria too, of shaving the head and wearing on occasions large wigs; perhaps it enabled one to be cool in the ordinary and beautiful or symbolic or impressive on the occasion. They span and weaved, these people, but they wore few clothes. They still hunted—what people does not?—but they were true 'mixed' farmers. They used mined flints and they had a few, a very few, copper harpoons, hooks, pins and needles. There are traces of walls round their villages (or to enclose their cattle) and of roads of wooden baulks, 'corduroy roads' across the mud.

Their dead they buried in cemeteries, large cemeteries with in one instance over two thousand graves, though with no sign of any particularly important grave, a chief's grave, among them. The practice of burying personal and treasured possessions with the body is still there and is in fact beginning to elaborate into the Egyptian's later quite obsessive preoccupation with the after-life of the dead. In the graves are models of women (wives or slaves) and of cattle, symbols of what the deceased will need for support and succour in the world to come; as for his dog, it went with him in person. There are many pots.

It is the nature of these models and of the pictures scratched on these pots that is revealing. There are figurines of female water-carriers and of men with their hands tied behind them: were there already slaves and captives of war, the beginnings of an organized use of them in irrigation? Then the scratched pictures show, besides animals such as elephant, giraffe, sheep, scorpion, a cow-headed female and a creature like Seth, the Egyptian god of night and the desert and all evil. At the same time in their liveliness and in some of their figures they are highly reminiscent of the Capsian rock

* The somewhat tricky subject of race we have left to the penultimate chapter.

paintings (Chapter 14) of North Africa and Eastern Spain. Here are connections both forward and backward in time.

Finally, of perhaps the greatest interest of all are the traces of these people's possessions that are not indigenous to the mud flats of the Nile valley at all. One of these is the mined flint. Others are the few copper tools, an occasional article in gold, malachite for eye-painting, vases of alabaster and basalt. A similar and indeed longer list could be made out for the first inhabitants of the even less self-supporting Tigris-Euphrates environment. Now this means trade and prospecting. And trade and prospecting mean human movement once more—for man never entirely settles down.

Whether trade began in luxuries or necessities, and what it was that neolithic people thought were necessities, are matters we can argue later.

20

Man Moves Again

THE reader may be becoming a little restive: a whole chapter on the Neolithic Age and not a word about Hill Camps or Long Barrows or Battle-axes or Lake Villages. We are coming to them: they are the result of the spread of the neolithic way of living and they occur largely after the originators have passed on to their new way of kings and writing and cities and states.

First we must guard against the wrath of the anti-diffusionists, of the common sense of those who say, 'It can't *all* have spread out from one place!'

It did not. Or rather, because certainties don't exist here, it is not likely. The Fertile Crescent is merely that place where it looks as if it began, where it grew up spectacularly—and whence, if it did all come from one place, it most certainly came. We have spoken indiscriminately of the discovery and use of wheat and rice and maize. The most likely places for those are the Middle East, India and Central or North America respectively. Are we going to suggest that the second and third discoveries waited for some missionary from Jericho or Badari to come and tell the benighted Indians, American or Asiatic, of the idea? Again it is possible, but not likely. If we are not Diffusionists we must be Evolutionists, and say that the time was ripe for the change, that it was the next inevitable step, that the changes in environment forced man to so adapt himself. That is unexceptionable so long as we do not become mystical and teleological about it, believing that such an end was implicit in its beginnings and inevitable. Until we know more, or perhaps for always, we must make our choice between the two views—or take a middle course, which should not be impossible or unreasonable.

Diffusion into Europe there undoubtedly was; that the communities of the Indus valley and the great rivers of China owed much to the Fertile Crescent is less likely. Before passing on we must say a word about those civilizations-to-be.

First the Indus valley and the famous sites of Harappa and Mohenjodaro. These are as much as four hundred miles apart and yet they are remarkably uniform as between one and the other. They are also remarkably uniform in themselves, planned streets and row upon row of neat little two-roomed box-like houses: the impression of a sort of well-organized slum. Egypt gained her unity by conquest and Mesopotamia never; it looks as if the huge plain of the Indus gained it by peaceful and political means. But it looks too as if the control was very strict and very effective: a safe but dull life for the ordinary man, proceeding utterly unchanged, as did the Aztec civilization much later, for generations.

But notice that we are talking in terms of civilizations and states and cities. The Indus valley is really out of our province. It must have had a Stone Age beginning and indeed there are material indications that it did; but the essential discovery is of something later. It grew no doubt as did the other river valleys, except that here had been something more like jungle to contend with, so that its irrigation and use may have been a longer and later job.

The same may be said of China: there also there has been unearthed a Bronze Age city culture with similar fertile river origins. Perhaps it was not so peaceful here—at Lungshan on the Yellow River the city walls were high. A distinctive find is thousands of 'oracle bones', human bones scratched with designs and characters: reminiscent of liver-divination but at least less revolting. China's civilization is traditionally and truly ancient; but that is a relative term, and it does not seem that she was first in the neolithic field or that, when she entered, her neolithic behaviour was much different from the common run.

Now for the Neolithic Europeans: poor relations of the successful Egyptians and Sumerians and their pioneering forefathers and yet destined to take over the lamp of progress from them and to make it burn most considerably brighter—just as those same early Egyptians and Sumerians took over from the successful and, to use an evolutionary term, too highly specialized paleolithic hunters. There are several waves of invasion into Europe, both of peoples and ideas, and more than one cause behind the movements. We must be careful to distinguish them.

Now there are several reasons for travel. We have stated the most generalized but the most fundamental: man's innate restlessness. There was also the desire to trade. There was the need to find virgin soil, *lebensraum*. There was the truly nomadic pastoralist's natural wandering habits and jealous aggressiveness. There was, perhaps, missionary zeal.

Room to live, room to sow and reap: the desire for that is the biggest pressure outwards. For we may remember those two-thousand-strong cemeteries of the Amratians, as earnest not only of care of the dead but of multiplicity of the living. The very fertility of the river valleys, by being matched by human fertility, was creating a shortage. The younger son must get out, and go somewhere no matter whether it was East or West or North or South. Not only that, but when in the centre the neolithic villages began to grow into Bronze Age towns these would demand more villages in turn to provide them with their surplus agricultural produce, and so on.

> To follow knowledge like a sinking star,
> Beyond the utmost bound of human thought.

Ulysses was also following adventure and, more practically, the finger pointing away from catastrophe. The same perhaps with the neolithic younger son. And it may be really true that where the stars and sun sink mysteriously below the horizon would be the direction most attractive and that West has always been, where it was possible, the favourite way to go. Here it was possible, and practically attractive. In the foothills of Anatolia was good soil, in the mountains the bright ores of metals, and beyond the mountains the sea and further land that could be seen. There was the crossing of the Bosphorus, the crossing of the Dardanelles—via Troy though not by more than a thousand years the Troy of Ulysses —and there was the prospect of the islands. So must this Anatolia —now Turkey, sometimes called Asia Minor, jutting out from the continent to which it only half belongs—have as it were lured the neolithic farmers and clever technicians across into Europe. Some (later) stayed on the islands: they found them no doubt quite virgin soil, for it is only now, in the neolithic, that man dares to sail far, still rightly afraid when somewhere or other he cannot see land. There, in the Cyclades, in Cyprus, in Malta, in Crete, they would

211

in due time found Bronze Age civilizations. Crete, the most famous of all, would also be invitingly open to Egypt.

However, we must follow with those who went earlier and further. Greece and the Balkans abound with small *tels* or mounds, that hide ancient villages in the same way as the Middle East abounds with large *tels* that hide towns. What was left behind there—the little votive figurines and the pottery, so unmistakably revealing to those who take the trouble to read the signs—all these show a definite connection with the Fertile Crescent. Northward up from Salonika

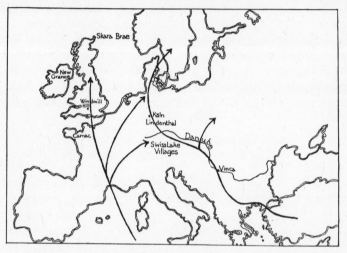

Invasion of a half-empty Europe: 'Danubians' and 'Westerners'
(*After Geoffrey Bibby*)

the slowly penetrating farmers must have come, over the difficult mountain pass beyond Skoplje and down the Morava valley to the Danube at about Belgrade. There met them an enormous expanse of fertile plain, not too densely wooded for their neolithic celts. They settled down for a while, perhaps metaphorically to recover their breath, and formed a community whose remains have been dug up at a site called Vinča. The Vinčans fished for sturgeon in the Danube, and had a habit of modelling faces on their pottery urns, though they did not follow the conceit of their Trojan cousins who made the lid into a sort of Phrygian cap.

Soon and inevitably these Danubians—for so they are called because of the route they took—fanned out into the great plain.

They found not a totally empty Europe but only those rather poor stay-at-home remnants of the great hunters, the mesolithic peoples clinging more or less to the water edges. These they no doubt mostly ignored, sometimes used, and occasionally married. Finally the Danubians reached the Rhine. Here is found another site, in 'the vale of the lime trees', Köln-Lindenthal; and it tells an interesting story. The lowest layer, that is to say the earliest, shows no huts or houses of any sort, only some long large buildings. The second layer shows a village of twenty huts, unfortified. The third layer, separated from the second, shows a fortified village of thirty-five huts. The likely interpretation is this. At the beginning men came across to new fertile land from an already existing village, cleared it, grew their crops, and stored them in the long large buildings. Then when all was successful they moved in and came to live. All

Memories of leather bags: Cortaillod pots

was peaceful, for there was plenty of room. When the land was duly sucked dry of its goodness they moved on once more. Later—it would have to have been twenty years at least but may have been several generations—the original or some other clan moved in again. And now land is not so plentiful or other peoples from other cultures and places are moving about, and the need for protection, at least for the cattle, is apparent.

And by now peoples from other places and with other cultures were indeed moving about. An important culture, which most certainly spread, is the *Cortaillod*. The name does not really matter very much, except that it shows the helpful ingenuity of the archaeologist. It is that given to the people's simple bag-like pots. They were copied, it is held, from containers made of leather. Therefore they were cattle-keeping people; and they contrasted with the Danubians whose pottery originated equally obviously from dried gourds, used typically in Mesopotamia. The Cortaillodians—let us call them West Europe Neolithic or plain Westerners; they will

213

be given many other local names in the not so helpful practice of archaeologists—the Westerners came it is believed from Africa, probably from one of those areas of the early beginnings of agriculture that we cited, Merimde. They crossed the Mediterranean at one of its narrow or island-beaded spots, found their way at length up the Rhône valley, and spread into Brittany, Switzerland, Great Britain and even up to Denmark. They did it, while the Danubians were also spreading, probably somewhere around 3000 to 2500 B.C. They become more well known than their contemporary infiltrators because they fitted their neolithic life into the local environments that they met in two rather spectacular and very different ways. They climbed either up on to the hills and downs, or over the water's edge.

First, what we would think the more healthy way. Windmill Hill in Wiltshire is a good instance, near to the later and very different Avebury.

Now here, archaeologists used to say, was obviously a 'hill fort' or fortified camp. But if fortified, why the numerous gaps in the fortifications, carefully left at regular intervals? Excavation, and thought, have given a better answer. Here were no signs of battle, as at the huge and later Maiden Castle, but only of a simple and peaceable people following their custom-bound occasions and no doubt hard but fairly pleasant yearly rhythm of living. Here was not a hill fort but a 'causeway camp'.* There had been, it is believed, no permanent village within the earthworks, but only the site of a yearly meeting place—not a corroboree, though no doubt there was that element of licence and release, but primarily an autumnal rounding-up of the tribe's cattle. The chalk downs were not exactly rich pasturage and the beasts had to roam widely; some too would have to be killed off before the lean winter. Once a year then they were brought to this centre, driven through the intentional and convenient gaps in the earthwork, and then tethered or penned. It must have been a time of great activity; branding, and disputing; milking, butchering, hide-scraping, tanning; love-making without and talk within. The place no doubt sounded to high heaven, by day and, at full moon, even by night; it may have stunk to high

---

* Maiden Castle probably *started* as a causeway camp. Another good English example is Hembury Fort, north of Honiton in Devon, a most uplifted and uplifting position.

heaven. But whatever the uncouthness, whatever the troubles and impending scarcities of the winter, a good time was surely had by all; for, whatever else, men find uplift of the spirit in meeting for an occasion. Nor presumably had these men been long enough in their English environment to learn to take their pleasures sadly.

Round the fringes of the Alps and particularly in Switzerland people of the same origin founded the other of the two ways of living. They sunk innumerable piles at the edge of the lake or swamp and built villages over the water.

Now this seems an elaborately difficult and curious thing to do. It is a sort of extension of the mesolithic habit of living near the water; and it continues over the centuries on these sites right into the Bronze Age; it flourished at Glastonbury in England when B.C. had changed to A.D., and it flourishes still in the East Indies. Protection from marauders and enemies is usually cited as a main reason. But it is not likely that there was much of this danger when these villages began. Safety from wild beasts may have been a reason. Or *lebensraum*—one had to clear less of the forest and could use for sowing or grazing all that one cleared. Cleanliness too perhaps, and an escape from mud. But also I cannot help thinking there must have been the urge of that fundamental human trait: a liking of water, and of looking down into water, of 'messing about in boats'.

Lake village: sometimes idyllic

These people ought also to have been happy then, and no doubt they were. But there are greater signs of tragedy. In particular there are recurring signs of destruction by fire. Paradoxically the ubiquitousness of water increased that risk, for fire now must always be near wood.

We do however get a picture of a well-organized and certainly not entirely barbaric life—and incidentally the picture is clearer than many for the curious and until these discoveries an unsuspected reason, that permanent immersion in mud or water will preserve many things that would have long ago disintegrated in the air. Organization is implicit in the very building of such a village-on-stilts. Then there was discovered the remains of the boat that had sunk with its too great load of boulders that were intended to have been put round the piles. With curses or with laughter? surely not with drowning since all must have been as good swimmers from childhood as are the present lake-livers of New Guinea. There was discovered the remains of fishing nets, of baskets and raffia mats, of wooden cups and ladles, of skeins of spun flax. There was much hunting and much fishing—these people would have been fools to despise the practices of their predecessors—but there were cattle and there was unleaven bread.

Finally two sites to complete the picture, the picture, that is, of the first two big slow waves of the 'colonizers' of Europe, who by 2000 B.C., long after they had started, very long after the new way of life had begun in the Middle East, had pretty well opened up all Europe. One is at Skara Brae in the Orkneys, the other on the east coast of Denmark.

Skara Brae has been called the Pompeii of the North, though it certainly is not so big. Sand and not larva was the preservative. Its distinction is that it is likely to have been pretty well buried even when its people lived there, only the smoke from the peat fires of the little cluster of seven stone huts showing to any unlikely visitor. The inhabitants had found a new use for kitchen-midden refuse— and no doubt earth too. The seven houses were connected by a low narrow winding passage and the whole conglomeration was covered over as a protection from the eternal bitter winds. There are no trees in Orkney but much slate-stone. The furniture is made of this stone therefore; a dresser, two beds by the wall with a niche for personal possessions above. Sunk into the floor are troughs—

to hold water, perhaps to heat water by the age-old method of dropping in fired stones. The fireplace is in the centre. Each house has two extra rooms: storehouse and lavatory with a drain. This accident of indestructible furniture allows us to see how far the New Stone Age, even in the distant and uncivilized North, could progress.

The other site is Barkaer, not far from the classical kitchen-midden sites. Here is a bigger colony, perhaps two hundred strong, and houses not in a huddled heap but strictly in row with a cobbled street beside. Indeed there is something on a small scale of the slumlike uniformity of Harappa. But at least there is no contrast as there is on the Indian site of the rich man's house; here is not

The stone furniture of Skara Brae

proletarian plus oligarchy but by the look of it simple egalitarianism. There are querns for corn-grinding and prodigious stone axes that can, it is reported, fell an eight-inch tree in eight minutes.

On a hill beside this neolithic village two pits had been dug. They were not graves. In them were found amber beads and two thin copper pendants. Now amber was local but prized: it is not only beautiful but it has *mana*, insects sometimes strangely embalmed within it, and the magic power to attract (the Greek word being *elektron*). As for copper, it was very scarce and must have been traded from afar. . . .

These precious gifts to the earth were likely to have been a sacrifice.

21

Light Thoughts and Dark

I F PALEOLITHIC MAN wandered because he had to, Neolithic
Man wandered as often as not because he wanted to. That hardly
applies to the early farmers, of whom we have taken as typical
the Danubians and the 'Westerners', but it does seem to apply to
what we shall call the Beaker People, the Battle-axe People, and the
Megalith Builders. These were neolithic people with ideas. We may
be able better to understand the urges that moved them and their
like if first, in this chapter, we consider neolithic ways of thought.

The man of the New Stone Age had plenty to impress his imagination and stimulate his thoughts, different mostly from those that
had stimulated his predecessors. Paleolithic Man drew, thought and
ate animal. Did then Neolithic Man draw, think and eat plant? He
hardly drew at all—his imagination was not stirred in that way.

He was quite probably stirred to music. There may have been a
paleolithic pipe—there are claims for such—but there must certainly
have been a neolithic stringed instrument, if for no other reason than
that the bow had been invented. The bow is almost a musical
instrument as it stands, just as it is a fire-raising one if you twist its
string round a hard stick to make the stick twirl and create friction.
Mute half a bow string and you have a note an octave higher—and
the human ear must be attuned to recognize and respond to that,
and a good deal that is more subtle than that, by the elementary
process of response to physical environment, which is not to belittle
an ear for music. Response to rhythm must be an inevitable accom-
plishment too. The drum, the stretched skin, might well have been a
hunter's invention. By the time of the Bronze Age the harp and
zither, that simple instrument of strings stretched in diminishing
lengths, had been invented. It is possible to make some shells to
vibrate like a trumpet; and there is claim for a neolithic xylophone.

218

There would also have been a chance now for the recognizable song or chant or dirge, for language must have been greatly increasing in power and complexity. Not only was there more to do and more to explain but people were meeting more often, both within the tribe, as at Windmill Hill, or inter-tribally, as we shall see with the people of the megaliths. When you meet friends you are stimulated to talk, even a little wildly and flamboyantly at times; and when you meet strangers you are induced somewhat to examine and become objectively aware of your own particular language. Perhaps now and only for the first time, although speech is undoubtedly old, there comes a real increase in descriptive adjectives and adverbs, and the appearance of abstract words.

There are signs of the existence of tallies. If men owned possessions they needed to be able to count beyond the mere fingers of a single or a pair of hands. Nor would the consciousness of numbers be solely utilitarian: numbers do strike the imagination. Man was, in the words of H. G. Wells in *The Outline of History*,[12] 'wondering at the triangularity of three and the squareness of four, and why some quantities like twelve were easy to divide in all sorts of ways, and others, like thirteen, impossible. Twelve became a noble, generous, and familiar number to him, and thirteen rather an outcast and disreputable one.' An unlucky one in fact.

In one aspect at least it had become essential to get down to good hard practical calculation. For a long time man presumably took the seasons as they came, though he must have been overjoyed to see the tundra and the steppes burst into spring. Lunar months were familiar to him; the interval tallies with the menstruation of women. But the length of the year is in no way calculable from the lunar month. Indeed it is in no way easily calculable at all, a fact that may surprise us who have had it done for us for so long. The regular rising of the Nile, and of the other great rivers no doubt—this is a familiar story—needed to be prepared for and so to be predicted. The clever and observant Egyptians—or a clever and observant Egyptian—did the trick by noticing that Sirius, the bright dog star (in what we call the constellation Canis Major), after being invisible from the beginning of June reappeared in the east a few minutes before sunrise in July and at exactly the time of the beginning of the Nile floods.

We swing back to imagination. The times at which the

constellations climbed up over the horizon as the tilted earth swung
round the sun had for man a tremendous significance. So too had
the constellations themselves: here was another convenient tool for
omens and divination, a tool we have not discarded yet. And surely
it was Neolithic Man who began to give names to the constellations.
He was seeing the night sky more than his paleolithic ancestors—
and certainly more than his neon-lit descendants. He was watching
his flocks by night; and they hardly needed, or at least received,
attention all the time. No one could possibly look at Orion and not
see a great straddling giant with upraised arms and 'belt and sworded
hip'—and not, I think, alone in the dark with only his dog who would
not contradict him, be impressed and a little afraid.

Man, as we know, incurably personifies, and he did it with
the stars. In time he would notice something further, that there
were a few stars brighter than the rest which had an aberrant and
very individual movement: one was sometimes red in colour and
might be the god of war; one appeared at a time of romantic beauty,
the morning and the evening star, and might be the goddess of
love. Here perhaps, into the mysterious vault above, retired at times
the spirits that were behind the earthly realities. And lording over
the whole was the Queen moon at night (controlling the genetic
life of women) and the King sun by day. We see dimly the poet-
thinker successor to the cave artist—an earlier and less articulate
shepherd King David—observing and inventing with a rising
excitement; and then using the growing power of vocabulary to
expound and explain, to tell the stories that we now call fairy-tales
and myths.

Nevertheless, it *was* the plant, and the behaviour of the plant,
that stirred his imagination most profoundly. Or rather it was the
fertility of the earth that impressed him, as witnessed by him in the
sprouting and ripening of the corn and also for that matter the
regular giving of birth by his ewes and cows and mares, a ripeness
and fecundity which he was now controlling in an active partnership
with nature. But what a precarious partnership and what an awe-
inspiring one! In spite of reserves—and how often can the neolithic
people have built up large reserves?—the primitive agriculturist is
in some ways more completely, more frighteningly, dependent upon
the vagaries of nature than the primitive hunter. A crucial month or
so without sun, or one without rain, will not kill off all the animals,

but it may irreparably damage the crops. Hungry, wilful and imaginative man was inevitably going to invent methods for improving his control. What did you do if things went wrong? How did you prevent them going wrong? Or keep them right? We should not expect the answers to be scientific.

Rather, men took to themselves the comfort of symbolism, that shaded into magic. The Earth in giving her increase was surely like a mother giving birth to her child; indeed the Earth was a mother, the Great Earth Mother. The symbol of fertility then was the mother, or those female parts that had to do with generation and suckling. The male part also obviously had its significance. Hence the female figurine and the phallic symbol—which incidentally may not be quite so frequent as the Freudian, who can see it everywhere, would imagine. Man once again was not squeamish or prudish in such things—why should he be?—nor was he pornographic, or if so only secondarily and incidentally. He was simply, according to his own lights, being practical, and doing all he could to help.

There was more to it, unfortunately much more to it, than that. We have seen that man was leaving the crude coercion of magic for the gentle persuasion of oblation and sacrifice. Rather, he was learning to combine the two. Nor in truth was the persuasion gentle, at least not in its execution.

One form of offering may have led to another and greater. For a long time as we know men had been furnishing their dead, especially their revered and important dead, with provisions for the journey in or to the other world. The custom was growing in neolithic times to inter the important beings elaborately, in fact to heap a great mound or barrow of earth above them. They would not dig deep for this for they had not the tools; but they would dig wide. If they left with the dead an urn of the great new food, the seed of corn, such of it as was spilt or blown would fall on ideally prepared ground. The next season it would appear, flourishing.

Did then the life-giving grain proceed from the death of a man? Certainly life proceeded from death and interment, for did not all life die in the autumn and the seed fall into the earth, and did it not rise from death in the spring?

Another thing. Man could influence nature. His sins for instance would make the poison deadly in the ordeal, the fire burning, the water scalding; if his sin was not expiated a murrain came upon the tribe. Was not this universally true, both positively as well as negatively? Vigorous man, vigorous nature; sinning or failing man, weak and unrewarding nature? This would be most particularly and spectacularly true with the important person, the chief. And in the Fertile Crescent at least, in fact wherever social organization was becoming a necessity, the important person was most certainly arriving.

The reader may again be growing restive. All this he may feel is no more than special pleading for the well-known theme of Frazer's *Golden Bough* that primitive agriculture all over the world has been bound up with sacrifice, the ritual murder of human beings. All this is a top-heavy argument on too slender foundations.

But that is not so. The reasons guessed at may be the wrong ones; but nevertheless the facts are too well attested: with the sowing of the seed and the reaping did grow up some monstrous rites. Sir James Frazer may have drawn the wrong morals from the evidence he collected; he may have regarded the primitive mind with something of a pitying superiority such as no modern psychologist, more aware of the illogicality of the unconscious, would ever dream of adopting. But that does not invalidate his findings—and, to turn the tables, the modern psychologist when he approaches anthropology is able to beat his own record of talking on occasion some pretty pretentious nonsense, even the great, the truly great Freud not excluded. I am not alone in believing that.*

For that matter, in case we seem to be protesting too much, most prehistorians do accept Sir James Frazer's findings. They usually dismiss them however in a paragraph or so. They cannot be so dismissed: that the introduction of agriculture brought to man the masochism and self-torture of these practices is a major event in his story.

We must do our best to understand. By some means or other— and I think it was more likely to be via symbolism than by any apparent practical demonstration such as the barrow burials— man got it firmly fixed into his head that only by the shedding of blood could the crops prosper, that payment by death had to precede the reward of the vernal renewal of life.

Essentially of course he was completely right, startlingly pre-

* *See* for instance Adrian Coates' *Prelude to History*[38] or Leslie Paul's *Nature into History*.[16]

scient. There is a cycle of life, one form depending on the death of a preceding form in the chain: the birth of spring will not come without the death of autumn; the grasses grow the better on the death and corruption of flesh. Man's tragic mistake came from his arrogance, the conviction that it was *his* actions and example that would magically influence nature—coupled at the same time with his fear and anxiety, his inability to believe that nature would be sufficiently beneficent without his prodding her, his bribery and bullying of the spirits that lay behind her.

The elaborations and ramifications of the whole business are prodigious: we can take only a few chosen glances. We do not know whether the practices started in stark ruthlessness and became toned down, or vice versa. Sometimes one, sometimes the other no doubt. But the idea that the Head of the Tribe, by his behaviour, vested in himself the whole tribe's responsibility for the malaise or the health of surrounding nature does seem a likely primitive idea that could have grown out of paleolithic men's beliefs in the intense powers of sympathetic magic coupled with his passionate tribal consciousness. Here is indeed the penalty of greatness and justifiable uneasiness of the head that wears a crown. Whether or not in past and distant history the Chief has ended up a victim to the theories that he and his shaman assistants must have done much to foster, dying in his prime so that the crops and beasts should not suffer the baleful influence of his senility, or whether his instinct for self-preservation overrode from the earliest his instinct for religion and he quickly found a substitute, a 'scapegoat', we are never likely to know. In either case there is the spilling of blood. But apart from that it seems likely that the first kingly lives must have been at the very least lives of incredible burden. The Chief was like the woman at menstruation, only more so. His *mana* was terrific, his spiritual voltage most dangerous. He must never touch the ground nor be shined upon by the sun lest his power and goodness, exactly like the current from a battery, should be drained away either to the earth or to the heavens. His clothes, his hair, even his nail-clippings were so full of *mana* that they must never pass into profane hands. For the same reason he must eat off coarse dishes, for afterwards they must always be broken. He must sit for a time each day unmoving on his throne, so that peace and tranquillity may be imparted to his people. Alternatively he must sleep on his throne, but not lie down lest that should stop the winds to blow and the ships to sail. Obviously no unfortunate being suffered all these disabilities all of the time; and indeed there must have been parts of the earth, though perhaps not many, that never suffered from the tortuosities of the first barbaric farmers' and king-makers' minds. But many must have suffered much of the time.

Some chiefs no doubt suffered the final fate. But whether the victim was truly royal or as substitute had had royalty briefly thrust upon him, I think we can be fairly sure that he usually went to his death quite willingly: drugged with passionate belief if not drugged physically. Perhaps the idea of a substitute was an original one: a passion for symbolism, a feeling that as it were an actor in the central role was not only as good an idea but better.

Whether this makes it all less tragic, or more, I do not know. It seems to have been inevitable that man should torture himself, or at least subject himself to disabilities and discipline, should *not* please himself: as we saw, that is the outcome of possessing a mind above the animal's and a conscience and a sense of morality and of the good of the many. But that the supposed good of the many should have been so terribly enforced at the expense of the one is something that we should never have guessed and is a part of truth that we need to realize. Here is a description from *The Golden Bough*. It is of the Khonds, a Dravidian race in Bengal, who purchased children so that at maturity—and after being brought up with affection and great deference—they might be sacrificed for the benefit of the crops, in particular the turmeric which 'could not have a deep red colour without the shedding of blood'. The account of what happened to these victims or Meriahs as they were called was taken from the reports of British officers who in the middle of the nineteenth century were engaged in putting the practice down.

'The mode of performing these tribal sacrifices was as follows. Ten or twelve days before the sacrifices, the victim was devoted by cutting off his hair, which, until then, had been kept unshorn. Crowds of men and women assembled to witness the sacrifice: none might be excluded, since the sacrifice was declared to be for all mankind. It was preceded by several days of wild revelry and gross debauchery. On the day before the sacrifice the victim, dressed in a new garment, was led forth from the village in solemn procession, with music and dancing, to the Meriah grove, a clump of high forest trees standing a little way from the village and untouched by the axe. There they tied him to a post, which was sometimes placed between two plants of the sankissar shrub. He was then anointed with oil, ghee, and turmeric, and adorned with flowers: and "a species of reverence, which it is not easy to distinguish from adoration" was paid to him throughout the day. A great struggle now arose to obtain the smallest relic from his person; a particle of the turmeric paste with which he was smeared, a drop of his spittle, was esteemed of sovereign virtue, especially by the women. The crowd danced round the post to music, and, addressing the earth, said, "O God, we offer this sacrifice to you; give us good crops, seasons, and health"; then speaking to the victim they said, "We bought you with a price, and did not seize you; now we sacrifice you according to custom, and no sin rests with us."

On the last morning the orgies, which had been scarcely interrupted during the night, were resumed, and continued till noon, when they ceased, and the assembly proceeded to consummate the sacrifice. The victim was again anointed with oil, and each person touched the anointed part, and wiped the oil on his own head. In some places they took the victim in procession round the village, from door to door, where some plucked hair from his head, and others begged for a drop of his spittle, with which they anointed their heads. As the victim might not be bound nor make any show of resistance, the bones of his arms and, if necessary, his legs were broken. But often this precaution was rendered unnecessary by stupefying him with opium. The mode of putting him to death varied in different places. One of the commonest modes seems to have been strangulation, or squeezing to death. . . . In one district the victim was put to death slowly by fire. A low stage was formed, sloping on either side like a roof: upon it they laid the victim, his limbs wound round with cords to confine his struggles. Fire was then lighted and hot brands applied, to make him roll up and down the slopes of the stage as long as possible; for the more tears he shed the more abundant would be the supply of rain. Next day the body was cut to pieces.'*

* Taken from *The Golden Bough*, 1929 abridged edition, Ch. 47.

The flesh was then distributed with great despatch and each landowner buried his piece with ceremony.

Here is a description by the Jesuit priest Bernardino de Sahagun, who saw these things, of the Aztec 'pascal festival', wherein they sacrificed a youth, specially chosen and without blemish.

'The youth chosen for the coming year was carefully trained to play the flute very well, to gather and bring in the "smoke-sticks" and the flowers, as is the custom among chieftains and courtiers; they also taught him how to swallow smoke and smell the perfume of flowers, walking about as do the nobles and people of the court. . . . The one appointed for the sacrifice at the next festival of this god was greatly venerated by all those who met him. If, due to the good treatment (good food) he grew stout, they would make him drink salt-water to keep slender.

The young man thus chosen to die at the next feast went through the streets playing the flute, carrying flowers, and smoke-sticks. He was free to be out day and night wherever he chose to go in town; he was always attended by eight pages, dressed like those of the palace, and he himself was given elegant and precious clothing by his master, for henceforth he was considered as a god himself. His whole body and face were anointed: his head was adorned with white chicken-feathers pasted on with resin: his hair was allowed to grow to reach the waist. After he was all dressed they adorned him with a wreath of flowers called izquixuchitl, and a long garland of the same was fastened on both shoulders. . . . On the legs he wore golden rattles, which sounded at every step. His feet were clad in elaborately painted sandals, which they called ocelunacace. Thus the youth was clothed for the first part of the year. Twenty days before the feast these clothes were changed; they washed the dye off his skin, and they married him to four maidens, with whom he lived for these last twenty days of his life. . . . Five days before the sacrifice they worshipped the young man as one of their gods. . . . After (the) fourth day they placed him in a canoe in which the king was wont to navigate, and which was covered by an awning; with him went his four wives, consoling him. . . . They took him to a small and poorly decorated temple

226

which stood near the highway outside the city at a distance of almost a league from it. As they reached the foot of the Cu, the young man mounted the steps by himself, and on the first one he broke one of the flutes he had played on during that past year of prosperity; on the second one another, and so successively until he had broken them all, and thus reached the top. There he was awaited by the Satrapas or priests who were to kill him, and these now grabbed him and threw him onto the stone-block and, holding him by feet, hands and head, thrown on his back, the priest who had the stone knife with a mighty thrust buried it in the victim's breast and, after drawing it out, thrust one hand into the opening and tore out the heart, which he at once offered to the sun. In this manner they killed all those who were offered to Tezcatlipoca.'*

This is mankind gone mad, one idea become an obsession. There are many parallels, in these and other descriptions. The victim is trained and petted; he is garlanded or hung with greenery; he is processed and worshipped; finally, drugged or dedicated or both, he goes to his doom. He is personifying—what? A corn-spirit, a king, a king-god, a god that dies that all may live? The people do not perhaps know now, or never did know—it is all a little confused. But they do know that it all has to be done.

Sometimes the sacrifice was an animal, into which the spirit of the corn or of vegetation was held to have entered—it could be, by some kink of the imagination, the littlest and least significant of creatures, even the wren, for instance, christened for the occasion a king. Sometimes the sacrifice was no more than a model, made significantly of dough, that is of corn. Such rites have come down to us and to civilization, their origins mercifully forgotten in a hundred customs of mumming and processing and the eating of special cakes.

Somewhere between the two extremes of innocent tomfoolery and the blood-obsessed rites of the Aztecs, somewhere at the back of all this variety on a single theme, lie the practices of the first agriculturists.

* Taken from *Primitive Heritage*.[27]

22

Forceful Travellers

ALL IS not darkness. Return to the great journeyings of the Neolithic Age, and we find that the ideas that moved these people were sometimes as innocent as a commercial traveller's, as healthy as a hiker's, a rather belligerent hiker no doubt, as forcefully benevolent perhaps as a bible-puncher's. The last is the least authenticated: what moved the megalith builders is still mysterious, but it was something most compelling.

First this stressing of the movement of people must be explained. It is of course true that the change from hunting to food producing did give mankind the chance to settle down and to form a home and so a civilization. But his settling is not so entirely settled. In many ways it is ourselves, in spite of our holiday trips and our aeroplanes, who are the settled people, so much so that we find it hard to enter into the way of thought of men less lightly held. There are people today, such as the North African Takrouris described in A. D. di Parajno's book *A Grave for a Dolphin*,[39] who spend a lifetime making a religious pilgrimage. They may settle down for a year, five years, ten years; but in the end and inevitably, unless death intervenes, they will pull up their shallow roots and go on. Geoffrey Bibby[10] quotes with approval from a presidential address by the late director of the Norwegian Museum, A. W. Brøgger: 'The truth is quite simply that it is *we* who have had our conception of distance destroyed. For the men of the Stone and Bronze Ages distance was no object. They knew no frontiers, needed no passport or identity papers or tickets. The earth was free, the world lay open, and they wandered across it as though a thousand miles was nothing but a joyous adventure.'

Three great movements then to close the Stone Age: of the Beaker People, the Battle-axe People, the Megalith Builders. All three are predominantly movements into Europe, though the last in particular is pretty well world-wide. It would be possible to choose for description movements elsewhere, across the Pacific, down the length of the Americas. But they would drag us much further into post-neolithic times in the rest of the world, and they would be neither so well documented (or rather 'artifacted') nor so significant. For in the history of the world that is to follow it is Europe, it is Western civilization, that matters: by no means solely, but supremely. Movement stirs up mankind and the ideas of mankind as surely as does a spoon stirs a cauldron of jam: European civilization would not have been the same if there had been no invaders raising beakers to their lips, wielding and proudly wearing battleaxes, or building dolmens and cromlechs and chambered long barrows.

Megalith means large stone. It is fitting that the last of the Stone Age men should also have been builders in stone, though a very different stone, that they should once more have seen great significance in stone. There is nothing surprising in the fact that men should have uplifted and made use of the great slabs of granite and the like that sometimes lay bare on the hills they frequented—what more natural than to upraise one as a monument and a commemoration, as Jacob, a great stone raiser, did, to mark Rachel's grave or his covenant with Laban? But the extent to which such a simple practice elaborated itself is surprising. I do not think that early men ever did anything by halves; there seems even, to us more reasonable people, an element of hysteria in many of their practices.

Megalith is Greek and so too is *trilithon*, the typical three-stone arch or lintel which is the architectural distinction of such grand efforts as Stonehenge. The other terms however are Celtic, for these monuments were often in the country where the Celts came, and stayed, and they were always sufficiently impressive, at the least, to be given names. It is useful to be aware of them:

a *menhir* is a single upright stone;
a *dolmen* is a table stone, a single huge slab supported by up-
    right ones;
a *cromlech* is a circle of stones, possibly trilithons but more
    often menhirs.
There are also long straight alignments of upright stones.

229

The dolmen comes first in importance, because it is the remains of a grave. It is indeed a sepulchral chamber; orginally it housed a body or bodies and it may or may not have been covered over with earth or stones. It is the poor substitute for—either the crude fore-runner or the decadent copy of—the chambered barrow.

We come to the barrow or tumulus familiar to most people of Europe, to be seen over the downlands and moors and hills. Shortly, these are of three types, the round barrow, the unchambered long barrow, and the chambered long barrow. The first, the most common in England, covers typically a Bronze Age burial, when men cremated their dead—it is out of our province. The second is not later but earlier than the megalith builders: it covers no great stones and is really no more than a mound above a charnel house—the bones for

Menhir, trilithon and dolmen

instance of the Windmill People whom we surveyed in the last chapter but one, enjoying their meeting on the downs.

The chambered long barrow on the other hand, the elaborated dolmen, the typical work of the megalith builders, is a major feat of architecture and communal effort. It is essentially a room approached by a long stone-lined passage, both of them roofed over. The chamber may be domed or it may have small chambers leading out of it; the dome at New Grange near Dublin, a magnificent specimen, is 20 feet high, the outer dimensions—it is a heap of stones not earth—being about 200 by 80 feet and its external height, no doubt sadly diminished from the original, 45 feet. Round this particular grave were originally placed thirty-five upright stones, each as high as a man. The more usual surround was a dry wall of a few feet high.*

* Chambered barrows are *sometimes* round. For a recent synthesis see Glyn Daniel's *The Megalith Builders of Western Europe* (Hutchinson, 1958).

The whole thing was not completely covered and there was always access to the chamber: the passage was used for successive interments. Inside have been found up to twenty-six skeletons. In fact here is a *mausoleum*, a family vault, the successive ritual interments perhaps of a dynasty. With the human skeletons have been found the bones of sacrificed animals, pottery, flint weapons, beads and shells, and occasionally a weapon or ornament of bronze or gold —there might have existed more of these last had not the long barrows been favourite places for burglary (and often, by popular repute, losing your wits in) through all the ages since they were built.

Now come two points about these last great works of the Stone Age People, one of which is as unfamiliar as the other is well known. This type of monument, varying in order to fit the local environment

Section through 'New Grange'. The Irish passage graves run in a line roughly from Drogheda north-west to Sligo

or fancy, but always basically the same, can be traced spreading westwards from the Eastern Mediterranean up through the islands of that sea, up through Spain and Portugal and France, to the British Isles and Southern Scandinavia, and eastwards through Palestine and Syria and Turkey and Persia as far as India. It is a spread around the sea coasts and up the estuaries and across the promontories; never does it penetrate really far inland. The unfamiliar point is this. Neither the skeletons nor the artifacts found with them are homogeneous. The pottery and implements not only differ from area to area but in every case show a high degree of resemblance to the pottery and implements of the *nearest inland area* beyond the megalithic zone.

This discovery, long in being made and appreciated, can it is believed lead only to one interpretation. Here is not a tribe on the move. Here were not wandering traders, for what trader bothers to persuade his clients to change their way of burial or undertake major

231

building enterprises? Here can only have been people who were spreading an idea—in one word, missionaries.

That is a strange idea. But it does seem inescapable. 'Converters of the heathen' nineteen or so centuries before the birth of Christ, just as there were nineteen centuries after! Yet it is by no means so impossible an idea if we pause to think of all that we have learnt of how the mind of early man worked. Imagination is stronger than reason, and what the mind's eye sees is more impressive than the physical message: man's beliefs may often have been fantastic but they must also have been vivid, indeed vivid because fantastic. What then was it that the megalith builders so passionately believed?

Unfortunately we do not know. Was it the dark maze of sacrifice for the good of the crops that we described in the previous chapter? Possibly. Here is certainly obsessive care for the dead; here is the putting of the chieftain—he could hardly have been less—with great pomp into what many people have seen as a sort of replica of a house of the living. But how are we to tell whether perchance those chieftains were ceremonially murdered in their prime? We know that the idea of sacrifice suffused the mind of the primitive agriculturist—even the dawning idea of one supreme god could not stop that, for Abraham was willing to sacrifice his son. But archaeological evidence of it is not easy to distinguish: only an occasional sign of decapitation rather than natural death, as for instance with some infant skulls at neolithic Jericho.

At the least, great power, great *mana*, must have come out from those magnificent graves. Possibly, as H. J. Fleure suggests,[40] there emanated a sort of 'vital essence', a spiritual seed, to impregnate the new births to come—thus shadowing forth a belief in reincarnation and the transmigration of souls.

Perhaps the other typical megalithic effort, the cromlech or stone circle, will give us a clue. These, such as Stonehenge, belong in their full magnificence to the Bronze Age, when the use of metals had completely penetrated into Europe. But it is the same tradition, and even the most imposing of them do start in a less ambitious way in the neolithic times. Stonehenge starts as a circular earth rampart, an inner circle of holes—perhaps for libations to the Earth spirit— and a central stone, the Hele stone: there does throughout seem to have been a connection with sun worship, an alignment with the sun at midsummer day*. And yet we have to ask, what exactly is sun 'worship', and is this much more than saying that the makers of Stonehenge were agriculturists who were supremely interested in the changes and timing of the seasons?

The only other good clue is the carvings found on the stones. Lately the lines of a Mycenaean dagger have been found on one of the Bronze Age monoliths of Stonehenge—but that is a connection late in date. Other carvings are circular scrolls and spirals, and the crude delineation of faces. The late O. G. S. Crawford has recently written a book, *The Eye Goddess*,[41] wherein he traces the carvings and engravings on the megalithic monuments back to an origin in

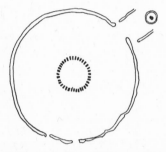

The neolithic Stonehenge: an outer rampart, an inner ring of 'bluestone' menhirs, and—outside and in the direction of the rising midsummer sun— a 'Hele Stone'

the cult practised typically at a certain temple at Brak in Eastern Syria, where were discovered an enormous number of figurine votive offerings whose chief feature is staring and fantastically exaggerated eyes. Mr. Crawford is content to call this, simply, a fertility cult, a worship originally of Baal and Astarte. But there is another book of similar patient tracing of evidence, *The All-Knowing God*,[42] by Raffaelle Pettazzoni, where the eye sign is taken, reasonably, as portraying a god who sees all and so is omniscient. This idea, says the author, is ancient and widespread; it is also bound up with the idea of a sky god and a worship of the sun, called as it often is 'the Eye of Heaven'. Here then, we can argue, are signs of a reasonably healthy megalithic religion: it has often been said by anthropologists that the sky religions are the religions of the nomads

* Though no proved connection with human sacrifice or with Druids, in spite of popular belief.

and the pastoralists, while earth worship is the religion of the agriculturists, the first being the more robust and the less introspective of the two. Yet the all-seeing eye is uncomfortably reminiscent of 'Big Brother' and for that matter of the worst and most vindictive aberrations of Christianity; and even the worship of the sun can be bloody and bound up with fertility rites—the Aztec Tezcatlipoca was a sun god.

We see then that there is hope for the megalithic religion being a not too dark and bloodstained one, but perhaps no very great hope.

Modellings, scratchings and carvings that spread round the world. In the centre: Eye Goddess from Brak; decoration from passage grave, New Grange, Ireland; bowl from Svinø, Denmark. On left, menhir at St. Sernin, France; on right, rock drawing, Wyoming, U.S.A.

One thing O. G .S. Crawford's book does show: how crudely conventionalized became the scratchings and carvings as they spread round the world from their centre of origin. 'We have,' he says, 'to deal with an evolutionary process by which a recognizable human face with a pair of eyes, eyelashes, eyebrows, a nose, and mouth, a fringe of hair and side-tresses, with perhaps a necklace and breasts below, disintegrated into a jumble of spirals, circles, multiple arcs, and zigzag and wavy lines.' It both disintegrated and degenerated. Like the Azilian stone-painter before him, the artist cannot in the end have known what he was portraying—only that this was the thing to do, the thing he had been taught to do, that had to be done. Compared with the cave paintings these carvings are lifeless—worse

234

than lifeless; strained, unreasonable, unintelligent as well as unintelligible.

There we must leave the megalith builders, to return to them for a moment at the end of the chapter. They were nomads, though in ships. They must have been very potent people.

Now we turn, shortly, to the Beaker People. What was potent about them may have been in their beakers: they may have brought beer to Europe. No one can prove it. But at least this can be said: why possess such beautifully made and lovingly patterned mugs if you have not something prized to put in them?

The Beaker People brought, more importantly and certainly, bronze to Europe. They do end the Neolithic Period, even for Europe. Yet they themselves used flint-headed arrows.

Pint pots? Two beakers found in
Somerset (Taunton Museum)

They are in fact traders-and-hunters. Perhaps in the beginning the two did tend to go together, because the hunter moves about the land: the Windmill People, who mined for flints as we saw was done above the Nile valley, are believed to have traded for antler-picks with what were left of the aboriginal hunters of Britain. The Beaker People settled particularly in Britain, in some parts being the first agriculturists to arrive. But let us give them another double name besides trader-hunters. They were smith-prospectors. They knew all about metals, all that there was to know so far. They made metal into weapons and ornaments; they sought it; they traded for it, taking in return jade and jet and amber.

Sir Grafton Elliot Smith[20] and W. J. Perry[43] were both, some thirty years ago, writing of 'the children of the sun', people from Egypt who wandered over the world, the Pacific included, prospecting for metal and gold in particular and spreading a worship of the sun. The theories of these two most enthusiastic anthropologists

235

are now largely discounted, though their books are certainly still stimulating. They laid much too much stress on the influence of Egypt and they did not differentiate between the megalithic builders and the traders. The truth is that the traders came after the megalith builders—just as in our times the trader came after the missionary, bringing proverbially the gin and whisky bottle and the gun after the Bible.

Nevertheless, by whomsoever it was, the metals were prospected

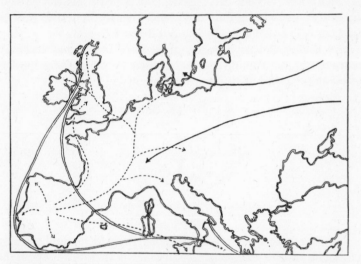

Late Neolithic Europe. Spread of the Beaker (dotted line) and the Battle-axe Peoples (black line), and of the megalithic 'missionaries'. (*After Geoffrey Bibby*)

for, and the useless gold as well as the useful copper and tin. Which however is a highly inaccurate statement from the point of Neolithic Man. To them gold was not useless. It was highly prized. Not prized as by us for its rarity, not solely for its beauty, but once again for its symbolism, its soft, pale, beautiful, indestructible brightness, indicative perhaps of the sun, certainly indicative once more of life. Messrs. Perry and Elliot Smith at least make out their case for that idea.

And I think we have here the answer to the question posed at the end of Chapter 19: what does early man trade in; and, if necessities, what are they? He trades in what he wants most. And he wants

236

most what leads to a more successful and more abundant life. Bronze that will make the new everlasting and resharpenable weapon is one of those things, that is plain common sense. But sea shells in shapes that suggest the fertility of women, and amber, and gold, are other of these things. They are *not* 'luxuries'. They are, mistaken or foolish though the desire for them may be, necessities, and necessities spiritual and not material. The gold necklet that bequeaths a feeling of mystical wellbeing to its wearer and at the same time a distinction in the eyes of the beholder; malachite that gives greenness and so life and is also the essential fashion to wear about the eyes; amber that not only has magic properties but beauty: those are the things that are traded about the neolithic world. The Beaker People, spreading in little bands from their home in Spain, more of the same small neat typically neolithic dark-white people, brought to Europe

Battle-axe heads

not only the bronze and took away the amber and the tin but fetched and carried a good deal of happiness and *fulfilment* in the process.

Finally the Battle-axe People. These were spreading at the same time as the megalithic enthusiasts and a little before the traders. They *are* a people on the move, and they moved from round about the Ukraine right across the Russian steppes to the Rhine and Scandinavia. Their graves are found by the thousand, and always the buried men have placed before their eyes the weapon that gives them their name. It is a stone axe, ground very smooth and with beautiful flowing lines and essentially copying the shape of the bronze axe of the Middle East.

These people were not agriculturists. They were herdsmen, nomads of the plain. Yet they settled down; for those who rove seem in the end to want to settle down. Their coming must have been an anxiety, perhaps a time of terror for the natives; yet, in spite of their famous weapon the newcomers seem mostly to have settled peacefully and to mix and absorb or be absorbed.

Not often absorbed however. Mostly they must have taken on an ascendency. For they seem a people of an aristocratic turn of mind, people proud of their weapons, who wear them as a badge of courage, and who, when they are Chiefs, go magnificently accoutred to their death. They are, it is held, the original Aryans.

Now there has been a great deal of nonsense talked of the Aryans, and do not let us add to it. But this much it is legitimate to say. We have talked of the darkness of the essential neolithic religion; we have left it open, though hopefully, as to whether the megalithic missionaries taught anything less superstitious or bloodstained. At least the Aryans were the forefathers of the Greeks; from them there will come in the end the free and enquiring and rational mind to check the dark growth of the first agriculturists' ghastly misconception. It is better for the soul, it seems, to breed horses rather than to grow corn.

23

Race and Language

NOTHING has yet been said about the races of mankind because so far as Stone Age Man is concerned they do not seem very important.

That may seem an outrageous statement. But it is true that *comparatively* the races of early man matter little, compared that is with what man did and thought; and if anyone can prove that Stone Age ability ran in any sort of line with modern nationality or even that Stone Age thought varied traceably with race at all, he is a remarkable person. The truth is that more nonsense is talked about race than probably anything else under the sun. The only significant and safe thing to say is that race is not and never has been anything static.

Quite legitimately we can treat it from an evolutionary point of view. Among animals a new species is likely to be created in the following way. A current species, thriving and under the consequent pressure of increase, deploys from its original habitat. As it spreads it will of necessity move by degrees into a different environment; and by a process of natural selection those creatures most fitted to the new environment will survive. It may happen that this new environment will, by the growth or appearance of some physical barrier, become cut off from the old and original. In course of time the denizens of the one and of the other may have diverged so much that should they meet again they either could not or would not interbreed: the isolated wanderers will have become a new species.

Much the same has happened with man, but not quite the same. There have never apparently been barriers complete enough and for long enough—nowadays of course there are no barriers at all. Consequently there has never been, since the Neanderthaler died out (if indeed even he was so different), more than one species of mankind. That is a surprising fact.

But there *has* been differentiation into what in the animal world we should call sub-species and what in the world of mankind we call races. It would be surprising if this had not been so: what white people without the artificiality of modern living, beginning with the elementary one of avoiding an existence wholly in the open, could thrive for generations in the tropics? Racial characteristics in fact must at the start have been no more than adaptations to particular environments.

Not that we can at this date always tell how the adaptations worked. Occasionally it is fairly obvious. For instance the man who lives in the blaze of the tropics is likely to have a dark skin. This is not an instance of the inheritance of acquired characteristics: father gets his skin burnt and son takes after him. Rather it must have been in its initial stages a negative matter: not until man got away from the blazing sun would 'sports' with white skins have a chance of survival, then possessing an advantage in a skin that could make more use of what sunshine existed. From which it would seem likely that original man was dark skinned. Another likely adaptation is to be thick-set and stocky in cold climates and thin-limbed in hot —the former type has less skin-surface for his bulk.

But how is one to define and categorize *race*, what is to be held as the crucial differentiation? As in all these things the definitions are artificial and man-made; and in this instance the difficulties are appalling—man's body is not a simple thing. The four most useful classifications are by:

> colour of skin,
> kind of hair,
> shape and size of body,
> form of head.

The first we have said something about. White seems a good sort of skin to have for living in cold climates, but yellow may be even better; how the extreme fairness of the Nordic type arose nobody knows.

Hair can be straight, showing as round in section under the microscope; or frizzy, showing as a flattened ellipse; or wavy, something between the two in section. It is the curly haired who as a rule have the most hairy bodies.

Of body framework we have also said a little. Small size may however be not always an inherited characteristic but a result of poor living, which will disappear with the poverty.

Shape of head we have already met: *brachycephalic,* a man with a skull (looked at from above) short from back to front and so broad or round headed; *mesocephalic,* medium (a term not often used); and *dolichocephalic* or long headed.* This is a most useful classification and a great favourite with the anthropologists. It is in fact too useful; for having been made it tells you very little and it is doubtful whether it really possesses any racial significance. There are other things to be said about head-shape however: the contour of the forehead, the amount of eyebrow ridge, the size of the jaws and how much they stick out (the jaws, not the chin; it is called prognathism), the amount of room for brain, and the 'nasal index', which

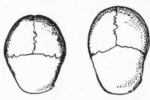

Skulls seen from above. *B*rachycephalic on the left.

is breadth compared to length from root at the forehead to where it meets the upper lip.

Now let us set out in irreducible minimum the racial types of today and then see so far as we can what were likely to have been the types in the beginning. There exist:

The Negroids
The Nordics
The Straight-Haired (Leiotrichi in science language)
The Mediterraneans or Dark-Whites
The Alpines
The Australoids.†

The negroids tend naturally to be long and thin, though they vary enormously, and not to be very hairy. They are indigenous in two groups, which were probably always separate: Africa, and the Pacific Islands called (merely Greek for *black* instead of Latin)

* As a mnemonic, 'brachy' and 'broad' begin with the same two letters. The cephalic index is breadth expressed as a percentage of length: *brachy,* over 80 per cent; *dolicho,* under 75 per cent.

† I am much indebted here to Adrian Coates' book already mentioned, *Prelude to History.*[38]

241

Melanesian. The first are usually prognathous, with broad noses, everted lips, and foreheads that are bulging like a baby's rather than with any torus or pent-house ridge; the second tend to the opposite in forehead and jaw. The extinct Tasmanians come in with the Melanesians; they had a very small brain-box. The Bushman we can just class with the African negroids, though his skin is browny-yellow rather than black. He too has a small skull, curiously low and narrow, and his hair is so tightly frizzed that it appears in little knots or peppercorns.

The Nordic hardly needs a description. He has been called 'this big, long-headed type'—not necessarily long-faced, though length of face and head do tend to go together. Thin-nosed. Not necessarily blonde. Hair to be classed as curly, that is to say not dead straight and round sectioned.

The Leiotrichi or truly straight haired comprise the biggest modern group, covering the Lapps and the Eskimos, the Mongols, the American Indians, and the Orientals, including the Malays. They are not necessarily from one origin, though we have seen that the Americas were almost certainly populated from Asia. Straight-hairedness does seem to be a true and fundamental race distinction, but it leaves room for wide variety in other ways: the Red Indian does not look much like the Chinee for instance. Generally, there is a lack of the torus, a round skull, and an unhairy body.

The Mediterraneans are also a wide group. Sometimes called dark-whites or brunettes; usually long headed; classed as wavy haired, and often very much so. They include the descendants of Ham as well as Shem, Egyptians as well as Arabian; also the Indonesians and probably the original inhabitants of Polynesia. Typically small and neat; small-jawed, small-faced.

The Alpine is round headed and often round faced. He is typically short and thickset, with strong brown hair and a sallow complexion. Besides the Alps his type inhabits now the Carpathians, the Caucasus and Asia Minor—where however he may develop a very tall head and a big nose. A mountain type perhaps, and not an early one.

Finally the Australoids. There are not many of them left: besides the Australian aborigines, jungle tribes in India, Ceylon and the Malay Peninsula. Typically they are long-headed, curly haired and hairy, dark brown skinned, wide nosed, prognathous, ridge-browed, fairly big and tall, sturdy.

Now what do we find in the beginning, that is to say when *Homo sapiens* has first arrived? Rather surprisingly, differentiation has already begun: skulls vary in shape, skeletons in sturdiness. There is for instance that Grimaldi skeleton, 'Aurignacian' but apparently negroid. Yet how can we know for certain; for a skeleton will not tell us the type of its owner's hair, or the colour of his skin, or even the turn of his lips. It is also true, again surprisingly, that in Africa there has been so far found no skeleton that is typically and unmistakably negro until mesolithic times, something nearer to the Bushman being much more common.

However in the Late Paleolithic the differences in *Homo sapiens* are not really great. We find the primitive traits we should expect to find, prognathism and pent-house ridges, though nowhere as near pronounced as with the Neanderthaler. Skeletons are usually sturdy, skulls nearly always narrow. Skin we should guess to be brown, in neither extreme of black or white; hair too to be of the middle type, neither dead straight nor woolly, and plentiful since man is after all a mammal. All that adds up, quite definitely, to something very like indeed to that primitive person the aboriginal Australian.

If then we wish to visualize the paleolithic hunter, the Australian aborigine is probably a pretty good model: darker and thinner perhaps in Africa, but never black; bigger and sturdier and lighter skinned where he is a cave man and near to the ice, though never as yet so white or fair as the modern Anglo-Saxon or Scandinavian. Early Stone Age *Homo sapiens* does not seem to have isolated himself sufficiently into groups for differentiations to have reached very far.

Mesolithic and Neolithic Man changed that. There began to form the village and the group of villages, the community that stayed put and inbred. By the end of the Stone Age the present pattern of race had probably approximately arrived—approximately, because as we have stressed it is a pattern that never stays still and in fact increasingly shifts and slides and wobbles.

If we wish to visualize the people of, say, the seventh to the third millenia B.C. we visualize the peoples of today, though clothed a good deal more primitively and decorated a good deal more barbarically. But if it is the neolithic peasant farmer in particular that we wish to visualize then we shall remember whence the culture spread and we shall see—typically, not invariably—a smaller, neater, smoother man than the hunter, dark-haired, still usually long-headed, and more universally brown-skinned even though his home may be the Swiss lake-village or the encampment on the English downs. That, though, is only the centre of the picture. The black-skinned man, the yellow, the white, must already have come into existence.

Finally, a page or two about the development of language. Unhappily a universal language of mankind is a dream only, at any rate so far as the past is concerned, for speech is a reaction to a particular environment as definitely as is skin colour or body shape.

Languages change by reason of the meeting and mixture of their users as much as do the users themselves; they may even be improved in the process. They tend to get shorn of their eccentricities and un-necessities: Anglo-Saxon is said to have been bettered in that way by the coming of the Normans, the lords using the barbarous language disdainfully, not bothering with the manifold inflexions, and the underlings not exactly liking to insist. This leads us to the undoubted truth that language is not synonymous with race: it may start that way, but the more movement there is the less it will stay so.

It is perhaps a pity but we must not become involved in philology. We are in fact barred; for we are concerned essentially with unwritten history, and without the evidence of writing we cannot tell what were the languages of the paleolithic and neolithic peoples. H. G. Wells' *Outline of History*[12] has a chapter on the subject, with helpful charts, and there are of course many less popularly written books. Here we may speculate just a little.

What for instance made the original languages as we might say 'come out different' from one another? Surely pure chance in the beginning. Shape of mouth and jaw will have something to do with it: people with short upper lips are less likely to use the sound 'p' for instance, and some mouths find 's' and 'th' difficult. For the rest, it is a matter simply of need. If you have nothing to do with a thing, then you will not have a word for it; conversely, for what is familiar your word is likely to be simple and short. Something can be learned from this, for instance the fact that 'horse' is short and much the same in most variations of the original Aryan language, or that it has a word for the supreme god that means 'sky-father': Zeus pater in Greek, Jupiter in Latin, Dyaus-pitár in Sanskrit.

The existence and the use of words can even be used as a guide to the character of a people, though it is a practice to be used with discipline and circumspection. That the English use the word *saucer* and the French *soucoup* and the German *untertasse* for instance: the first a casually used 'muddle-through' derivative from something else; the other two more logically precise, with the German word more clumsy. It is perhaps significant of an outlook that the Greek word for adornment, *cosmetikos*, is derived from their word for order, good order.

It is of course not only words that differ in languages but grammar and construction, and that fact too can be significant. Before writing came with its disciplinary influence much more use was made no doubt of the power to give meaning by change in tone of voice. Written Greek suggests a relic of it in its accents. But the Chinese group of languages shows it in extreme degree. The Pekinese form of Chinese is said to possess only 420 primary words, all monosyllables, and with these one has to make do, the listener understanding by the help of the context and in particular of the tone and pitch of the voice, grammar as we understand it hardly existing. Chinese is a practical language without much scope for metaphor: the people who originally invented it must have been a very different people from those for instance around the Fertile Crescent who invented the Hamitic and Semitic languages, rich and complicated, or the people of the Eurasian steppes who evolved the almost fancifully grammatical Aryan with its animistic insistence on a gender for everything (the sun is *he*, the moon is *she*, as is that wayward thing a ship).

Some metaphor however there must be in any language; some simile too. Indeed as languages grew these two must also have grown. From metaphor may even have come the birth of adjectives: the Tasmanian is said to have had no word for hard but only 'like a stone'. Similarly the simplest way to invent abstract words is to use concrete ones metaphorically or—to return to our favourite epithet for the mind of early man—symbolically: The *head* of this tribe is *tied* to the *life* of his people by his *sacred mission* and his *willingness* to *embrace* the sword.

It must have been in neolithic times that language really blossomed forth. Primitive man's speech has probably never been so poor and practical and unspiritual as travellers and missionaries have tended to believe, for it is the words that shadow forth belief that will be the secret and guarded words, too powerful to be uttered or too precious and vulnerable to be made known to the uninitiated. Paleolithic Man's speech may not have been greatly developed; it was not necessarily simple, for, as we saw in an earlier chapter, man does seem to have tortured himself with linguistic complication as he tortured himself in so many ways, but creaking and cumbersome, unco-ordinated in its syntax, lacking in abstract words, poor in the power to convey ideas. Neolithic Man on the other hand had many more interests, more possessions, more responsibilities, more jobs to do and to be taught. Each new job had its vocabulary—sowing, harvesting, milling; shepherding, breeding; sailing, boatmaking—and every new vocabulary gave chances for the poetically minded to use words allusively and metaphorically.

In particular, I think, man spoke allusively. The simple and imaginative and unspoiled mind has, time and again, shown that it loves to express itself not directly, but by parable, by saw and proverb and riddle, and by that trick of enhancing the meaning by representing it allegorically and indirectly so that the hearer has to use his own imagination before he can understand. It is the way some African natives have talked, the way the early Norse people talked— Eric Linklater has caught it in *White Maa's Saga*—the way the people of the Bible talked—Naaman the prophet in front of King David; Jesus to his disciples. The Book of Proverbs is full of the sort of thing, sometimes the second verse giving the key lest all readers shall not be intelligent enough:

> Take away the dross from the silver, and there shall come forth a vessel for the finer.
> Take away the wicked from before the king, and his throne shall be established in righteousness.

So perhaps, on a lesser and less exalted plane, Neolithic Man began to talk, delighting in confounding and stimulating his hearer, delighting in the power of words and of imagery. At its best it was the first poets and prophets talking, at its worst it was the Stone Age equivalent of the club bore and the sea lawyer.

Neolithic times saw trade in ideas as well as in those other things miscalled luxuries.

24

The Last of Stone

IT IS meet and right to take a man-made flint in the hand and to think thoughts deep but not pretentious or sentimental.

They used, the early people, stuff that lasted. So, fitly, their thoughts and culture remain indestructible, ineradicably embedded in our own. The Stone Age people were tough like their material, for they had to be. But they were not hard, nor were they cruel; though flint is sharp and makes a good weapon, war did not come easily into the world. That it did come, with the competition for living-room, must not sadden us. We must not be ashamed that man is the only animal which fights itself, if indeed it is strictly true. He is also the only animal noticeably altruistic.

His mind is not tough but tender. There was never a golden age of innocence; for man, as soon as he becomes fully human, has lost his innocence. He has his mind to help him, but he has his conscience to contend with and his imagination both to uplight him and frighten him. He is a mind-harried creature.

His progress is stupendous: from animal to man in a million years or less; from agriculturist to citizen, from stone user to metal user, in a thousand years.

The flint is cold but smooth, with a dull sheen. It has a way of fitting the hand. Ten thousand years ago, or a hundred thousand years ago, other hands have held it and shaped it. The shaper as he held it may also have sat back and thought: the next meal; since he was as prone to day-dreaming as we are, the next lovers' meeting, the next conquest, the next success. But sometimes his thoughts must have soared higher.

Or if not soared higher, then scouted wider, sunk deeper. We have tried to follow them—and in the process, I think, felt more

247

liking for the hunter than the reaper; he seems a more open character, a more heroic. But it was the later men who did the greater thinking. That they sometimes thought badly was their misfortune, and is still ours; the best we can say is that they went through a necessary stage. Nor can they have been wholly without light. Neolithic Man knew nature, even probably better than Paleolithic Man because he was in partnership with nature. He knew a summer morning and the sparkle of dew on gossamer, and the quietness of moonlight, and the thrust of the greenness of spring, and the sight of cloud shadows chasing each other over the bare hills; he knew these all more intimately and therefore more joyfully than ever we do.

He had, at the very least, sensitivity—as had also his forbears back to the beginning.

In this book I have tried to grind no axes, nor to overstate a case. Man may have had little religion by the time the age of stone was over; he may have been as far from acknowledging one supreme and loving god .as is a tottering babe from the firm step of the soldier or a light-sensitive animalcule from the keen sight of a hawk. But the beginnings are there; and in this context the same at least may be claimed: the beginnings are there. For man was from the start, and knew it, a creature of the spirit as well as of the flesh.

He was a creature, a troubled creature, of imagination. Not a mere creature of *our* imagination however. He did—and let us remember it—really exist.

Further Reading

I

Here is a list of the books referred to or quoted
from in the text, under their reference numbers:

1. *History of the Primates* by W. E. Le Gros Clark (Chicago: University of Chicago, 1955).
2. *Meeting Prehistoric Man* by G. H. R. von Koenigswald (New York: Harper, 1957).
3. *Early Man* by A. H. Brodrick (London: Hutchinson, 1948).
4. *The Prehistory of East Africa* by Sonia Cole (Baltimore: Penguin Books, 1956).
5. *Man the Toolmaker* by Kenneth P. Oakley (Chicago: University of Chicago, 1957).
6. *Man in Search of His Ancestors* by André Senet (New York: McGraw-Hill, 1955).
7. *Man on His Nature* by Sir Charles Sherrington (Baltimore: Penguin Books, 1955).*
8. *The Social Life of Monkeys and Apes* by Sir Solly Zuckerman (New York: Harcourt, Brace, 1932).
9. *Voyage of the Beagle* by Charles Darwin (New York: Dutton, Everyman edition).
10. *The Testimony of the Spade* by Geoffrey Bibby (New York: Knopf, 1956).
11. *The Inheritors* by William Golding (London: Faber and Faber, 1956).
12. *The Outline of History* by H. G. Wells (New York: Doubleday, rev. ed. 1956).
13. *The Miraculous Birth of Language* by R. A. Wilson (New York: Philosophical Library, 1948).
14. *Language* by Otto Jespersen (London: Allen and Unwin, 1922).
15. *Aspects of Language* by W. J. Entwistle (New York: Macmillan, 1954).
16. *Nature into History* by Leslie Paul (London: Faber and Faber, 1957).

* This and some of the other 'Penguins' have been published in other earlier editions.

THE STORY OF MAN

17. *The Lascaux Cave Paintings* by Fernand Windels (New York: Viking, 1950).
18. *Return to Laughter* by Elenore Smith Bowen (New York: Harper, 1955).
19. *The Golden Bough* by Sir James Frazer (New York: Macmillan, abridged edition, 1929).
20. *Human History* by G. Elliot Smith (London: Cape, 1934).
21. *Evolution in Action* by Julian Huxley (New York: Harper, 1953).
22. *The Sexual Life of Savages in North-West Melanesia* by B. Malinowski (New York: Harcourt, Brace, 1-vol. ed. 1934).
23. *Growing Up in New Guinea* by Margaret Mead (Baltimore: Penguin Books, 1954).
24. *Coming of Age in Samoa* by Margaret Mead (Baltimore: Penguin Books, 1944).
25. *Totem and Tabu* by Sigmund Freud (New York: W. W. Norton, 1952).
26. *What Happened in History* by Gordon Childe (Baltimore: Penguin Books, 1946).
27. *Primitive Heritage* edited by Nicholas Calas and Margaret Mead (New York: Random House, 1953).
28. *Journey Down a Rainbow* by Jacquetta Hawkes and J. B. Priestley (New York: Harper, 1956).
29. *Ancient Hunters* by W. J. Sollas (New York: Macmillan, 1924).
30. *The Painted Caves* by Geoffrey Grigson (London: Phoenix House, 1957).
31. *Just So Stories* by Rudyard Kipling (New York: Doubleday, 1912).
32. *Peasants and Potters* (Book III of *The Corridors of Time* series) by Harold Peake and H. J. Fleure (New York: Oxford University Press, 1927).
33. *Manners, Customs and Conditions of the North American Indians* by George Catlin (London: Stationers Hall, 1841).
34. *Primitive Mentality* by Lucien Lévy-Bruhl (New York: Macmillan, 1923).
35. *Primitive Religion, Its Nature and Origin* by Paul Radin (New York: Dover).
36. *New Light on the Most Ancient East* by Gordon Childe (New York: Grove).
37. *Digging Up Jericho* by Kathleen Kenyon (New York: Praeger, 1958).
38. *Prelude to History* by Adrian Coates (New York: British Book Centre, 1951).
39. *A Grave for a Dolphin* by A. D. di Parajno (London: Deutsch, 1956).
40. *The Natural History of Man in Britain* by H. J. Fleure (New York: British Book Centre, 1951).

250

41. *The Eye Goddess* by O. G. S. Crawford (New York: Macmillan, 1958).
42. *The All-Knowing God* by Raffaelle Pettazzoni (New York: Humanities Press, 1956).
43. *The Growth of Civilization* by W. J. Perry (New York: Dutton, 1924).

II

Of recent books on archaeology I think the best and most helpful is Geoffrey Bibby's *The Testimony of the Spade*,[10] which is a review of the discoveries in Northern Europe. Something similar on a worldwide scale, though rather more factual and technical, is Dr. Glyn Daniel's *A Hundred Years of Archaeology* (New York: Macmillan, 1950).

Another book not mentioned in the text, M. C. and C. H. Quennell's *Everyday Life in Prehistoric Times* (London: Batsford), is one very helpful to beginners, as is Gordon Childe's *What Happened in History*.[26] On Stonehenge: Professor R. J. C. Atkinson's book of that name (London: Hamish Hamilton, 1956); on ethnology: C. S. Coon's *Races of Europe* (New York: Macmillan, 1939).

As an introduction to and a liberal education in anthropology I believe there is still no better book than Frazer's *Golden Bough*.[19] For stimulating ideas on man's spirituality and early thought and religion, go to Leslie Paul's *Nature into History*.[16]

Index